W9-ARN-655

BIGGEST BOOK OF SEARCH & FIND®

Tony and Tony Tallarico

Kids**books**®

Copyright © 2004, 2019 Kidsbooks, LLC and Tony Tallarico

3535 West Peterson Avenue
Chicago, IL 60659

All rights reserved, including the right
of reproduction in whole or in part in any form.

Search & Find is a registered trademark of Kidsbooks, LLC

Printed in China
091901032GD

Visit us at **www.kidsbooks.com**

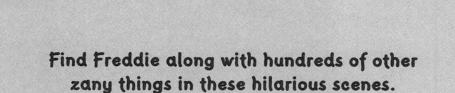

FIND FREDDIE

WHERE ARE THEY?

Find Freddie along with hundreds of other zany things in these hilarious scenes.

- ◎ Uncle Sam at the ballpark
- ◎ Cowboys on the beach
- ◎ Humpty Dumpty in Monsterville
- ◎ Flying fish in space
- ◎ Peanuts at the museum
- ◎ Rabbits at school
- ◎ Flying saucers in the Old West

. . . and lots more!

Find Freddie
at
Home
and...

- ☐ "8 Up" can
- ☐ Alarm clock
- ☐ Arrow
- ☐ Baseball player
- ☐ Baseball trophy
- ☐ Birdcage
- ☐ Bow tie
- ☐ Broken heart
- ☐ "Call Joe"
- ☐ Drum
- ☐ Elephant head
- ☐ Fake teeth
- ☐ Harmonica
- ☐ Hockey stick
- ☐ "How to Play" book
- ☐ "Junk Mail"
- ☐ Light switch
- ☐ Monster foot
- ☐ Orange and green lamp
- ☐ Paper airplanes (5)
- ☐ Peanuts
- ☐ Picture
- ☐ Popcorn
- ☐ Record
- ☐ Skulls (2)
- ☐ Straws (2)
- ☐ Sunglasses
- ☐ Telescope
- ☐ Thermometer
- ☐ Tire swing
- ☐ Yo-yo

Find Freddie
in
Space
and...

- [ ] Angel
- [ ] Balloon
- [ ] Basketball
- [ ] Bathtub
- [ ] Cannon
- [ ] Dogcatcher
- [ ] Doghouse
- [ ] Dragon
- [ ] Envelope
- [ ] Flying school bus
- [ ] Garbage truck
- [ ] Gorilla
- [ ] Hammer
- [ ] Mary Poppins
- [ ] Meatball
- [ ] "Meteor shower"
- [ ] NASA parachute
- [ ] Necktie
- [ ] Pencil
- [ ] Pink elephant
- [ ] Pinocchio
- [ ] "Planet of the Foot" (2)
- [ ] Polka-dot shorts
- [ ] Pyramid
- [ ] Red spray paint
- [ ] Rocking chair
- [ ] Scissors
- [ ] Slingshot
- [ ] Top hat
- [ ] Traffic light
- [ ] Trash can

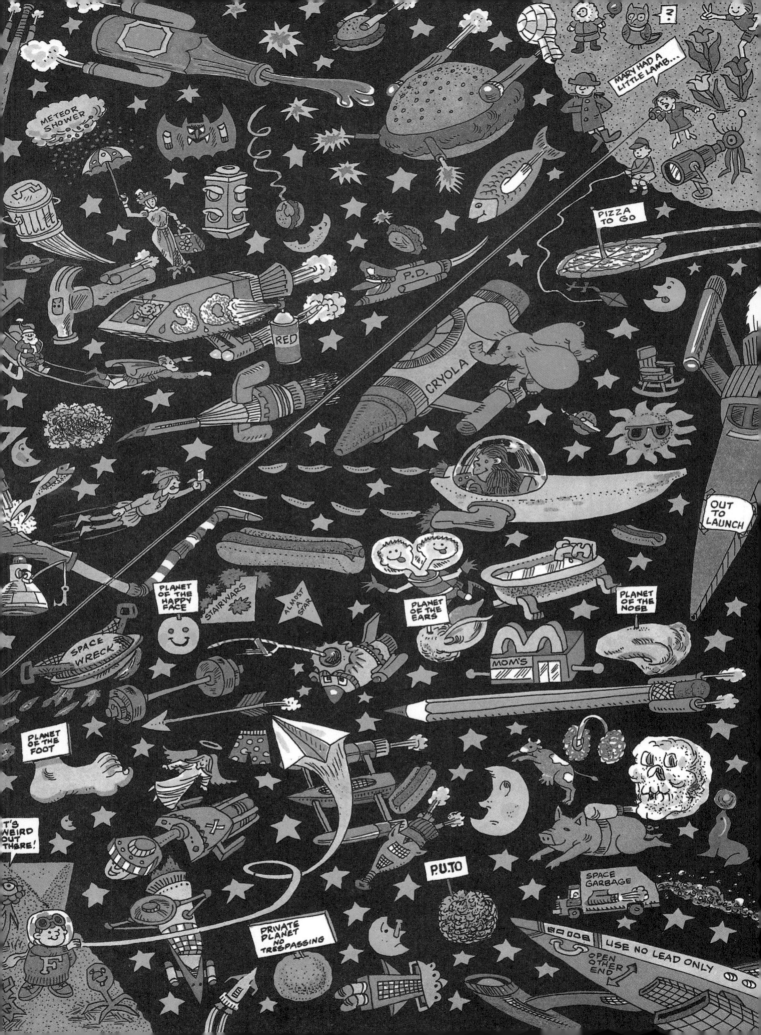

Find Freddie at the Beach and...

- ☐ Barrel
- ☐ Clothespin
- ☐ Duck
- ☐ Eight ball
- ☐ Elephant
- ☐ Fishing cat
- ☐ Flamingo
- ☐ Flying car
- ☐ "Fresh Sand"
- ☐ Giant sandwich
- ☐ Golfers (2)
- ☐ Handstand surfer
- ☐ Helicopter
- ☐ Horse
- ☐ Kangaroo
- ☐ Lighthouse
- ☐ Lion
- ☐ Mice (2)
- ☐ Motorcycle
- ☐ Open umbrellas (6)
- ☐ Radios (2)
- ☐ Rocket
- ☐ Rowboat
- ☐ Scuba diver
- ☐ Sheriff
- ☐ Shovel
- ☐ Snowshoes (2)
- ☐ Starfish (2)
- ☐ Strongman
- ☐ Tent
- ☐ Watering can
- ☐ Witch

Find Freddie
at
School
and...

- ☐ Air pump
- ☐ Barbells (2)
- ☐ Baseballs (2)
- ☐ Basketballs (3)
- ☐ Bench
- ☐ Briefcases (2)
- ☐ Broken windows (2)
- ☐ Butterfly net
- ☐ Cake
- ☐ Fish (2)
- ☐ Fishing pole
- ☐ Horse
- ☐ Jump rope
- ☐ Magic carpet
- ☐ Mail carrier
- ☐ Mouse
- ☐ Mud puddle
- ☐ Musical notes (3)
- ☐ Paper airplanes (5)
- ☐ Pillow
- ☐ Pumpkin
- ☐ Rabbits (2)
- ☐ Skull
- ☐ Soccer ball
- ☐ Surfboard
- ☐ Swing set
- ☐ Telescope
- ☐ Trash can
- ☐ Tug-of-war
- ☐ Upside-down bucket
- ☐ Window washer

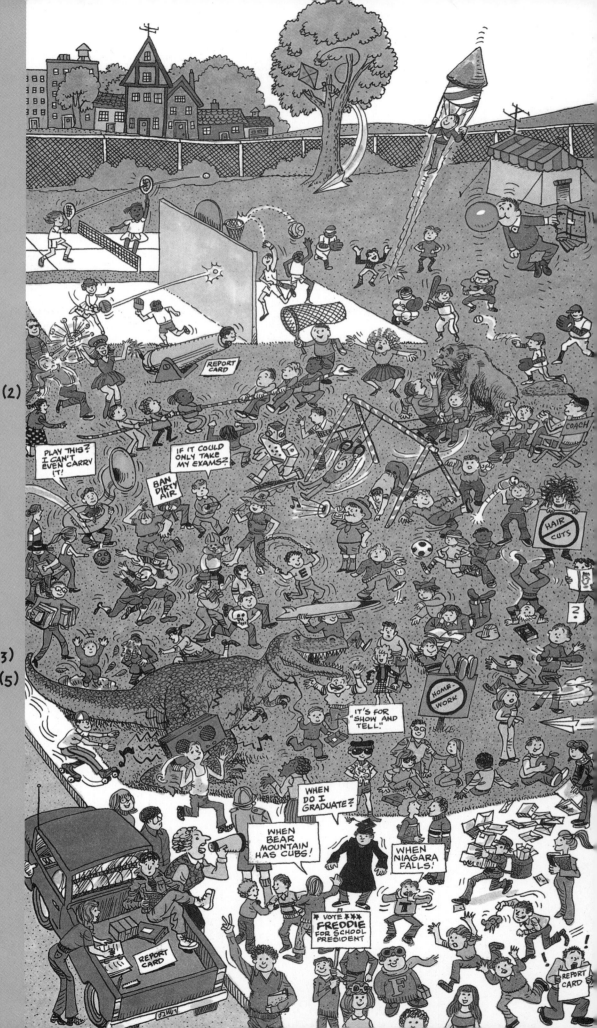

Find Freddie
on the
School
Bus Trip
and...

- [ ] Barn
- [ ] Baseball bat
- [ ] Basketball court
- [ ] "Clean Me"
- [ ] Dogs (2)
- [ ] Elephant
- [ ] Flying bat
- [ ] Football
- [ ] Frankenstein's monster
- [ ] Giraffe
- [ ] Horse
- [ ] Hot dog mobile
- [ ] Jack-o'-lantern
- [ ] Moose head
- [ ] Pig
- [ ] Pizza truck
- [ ] Rowboat
- [ ] Santa Claus
- [ ] Scarecrow
- [ ] Snake
- [ ] Swimming pool
- [ ] Tennis court
- [ ] Tent
- [ ] Tic-tac-toe
- [ ] Tombstone
- [ ] Traffic cop
- [ ] Turtle
- [ ] Umbrellas (2)
- [ ] U-shaped building
- [ ] Well

Find Freddie in
Monsterville
and...

- ☐ Broken heart
- ☐ Carrot
- ☐ Cowboy hat
- ☐ Flowers (2)
- ☐ "For Rent"
- ☐ Gorilla
- ☐ Hose
- ☐ Key
- ☐ Mouse hole
- ☐ Ms. Transylvania
- ☐ Mummy
- ☐ Number 13 (3)
- ☐ Octopus
- ☐ One-eyed monster
- ☐ Owl
- ☐ Parachute
- ☐ Pig
- ☐ Pile of bones
- ☐ Pink hand
- ☐ Pyramid
- ☐ Rat
- ☐ Scary trees (2)
- ☐ Skeleton
- ☐ Skulls (8)
- ☐ Stethoscope
- ☐ Three-legged ghost
- ☐ Tin can
- ☐ Tin man
- ☐ Trick-or-Treat bags (4)
- ☐ Weather vane

Find Freddie at the **Airport** and...

- ☐ Binoculars
- ☐ Birdcage
- ☐ Chair
- ☐ Clothespins (6)
- ☐ Football
- ☐ Golf club
- ☐ Green checkered pants
- ☐ Guardhouse
- ☐ Hammock
- ☐ Harpoon
- ☐ Hearts (2)
- ☐ Helicopters (2)
- ☐ Hot-air balloon
- ☐ Hot dogs (2)
- ☐ Ice-cream cones (2)
- ☐ Kite
- ☐ Laundry line
- ☐ Locomotive
- ☐ Lost wallet
- ☐ Manhole
- ☐ Paint rollers (2)
- ☐ Parachute
- ☐ Pear
- ☐ "Pequod"
- ☐ Pizza
- ☐ Roller coaster
- ☐ Skier
- ☐ Stretch limo
- ☐ Submarine
- ☐ Toaster
- ☐ Wooden leg

Find Freddie at the Ballpark and...

- ☐ Balloons (7)
- ☐ Banana
- ☐ Baseball bats (10)
- ☐ Basketball hoop
- ☐ Bicycle
- ☐ Binoculars
- ☐ Blimp
- ☐ Carrot
- ☐ Clipboard
- ☐ Cook
- ☐ Cowboy hat
- ☐ Crown
- ☐ "Detour"
- ☐ Dogs (2)
- ☐ Gorilla
- ☐ Kite
- ☐ Ladder
- ☐ Lawn mower
- ☐ Money
- ☐ Mouse hole
- ☐ Parachutist
- ☐ Periscope
- ☐ Policemen (2)
- ☐ Ripped pants
- ☐ Sombrero
- ☐ Sunbather
- ☐ Sword
- ☐ Tic-tac-toe
- ☐ Toolbox
- ☐ Trash can
- ☐ Turtle
- ☐ Upside-down fan

Find Freddie
at the
Museum
and...

- [ ] Airplane
- [ ] Alien
- [ ] Balloons (7)
- [ ] Bather
- [ ] Birdcage
- [ ] Birthday cake
- [ ] Doctor
- [ ] Doghouse
- [ ] Firefighter
- [ ] Fire hydrant
- [ ] "First Prize"
- [ ] Fishing pole
- [ ] Flying carpet
- [ ] Football player
- [ ] Guitar
- [ ] Headless man
- [ ] Hot-air balloon
- [ ] Ice-cream cone
- [ ] Jack-in-the-box
- [ ] Kite
- [ ] Knights (2)
- [ ] Long beard
- [ ] Magnifying glass
- [ ] Princess
- [ ] Quicksand
- [ ] Robin Hood
- [ ] Scuba diver
- [ ] Superman
- [ ] TV antenna
- [ ] Viking ship
- [ ] Watering can
- [ ] Whistle

Find Freddie
in the
Old West
Town
and...

- ☐ Angel
- ☐ Apple
- ☐ Artist
- ☐ Baby turtle
- ☐ Camel
- ☐ Car
- ☐ Fire hydrant
- ☐ Fishing pole
- ☐ Flowerpot
- ☐ Football
- ☐ Guitar
- ☐ "ICU2"
- ☐ Monster hand
- ☐ Mouse holes (2)
- ☐ Outhouse
- ☐ Pencil
- ☐ Periscope
- ☐ Piano
- ☐ Pink elephant
- ☐ Rabbits (3)
- ☐ Sailboat
- ☐ Saw
- ☐ Smoke signal
- ☐ Soccer ball
- ☐ Stop sign
- ☐ Sun
- ☐ Toasters (5)
- ☐ UFO
- ☐ Umbrellas (2)
- ☐ Upside-down sign
- ☐ "Wet Paint"

FIND FREDDIE   LOOK FOR LISA   HUNT FOR HECTOR   SEARCH FOR SAM

HUNT FOR HECTOR

WHERE ARE THEY?

Where's Hector?
You'll have to search through these
wacky scenes—and more—to find him!

- Cats at the Dog Mall
- K-9 secret agents
- Fencing dogs at the Olympics
- Fire hydrants in Dogtown
- Bones at the Hall of Fame
- Dancing dogs at school
- Hot dogs in space

. . . and lots more!

Hunt for Hector at the Dog Hall of Fame and...

- ☐ Baby kangaroo
- ☐ "Bach Beagle"
- ☐ Beard
- ☐ Birds (2)
- ☐ Chef
- ☐ Dog bowl
- ☐ Dogcatcher
- ☐ Dog stamp
- ☐ Elephant
- ☐ Eyeglasses (3)
- ☐ Fire hydrant
- ☐ Football helmet
- ☐ Hearts (3)
- ☐ Hot-air balloon
- ☐ Kangaroo
- ☐ Mailbag
- ☐ Moon
- ☐ Mouse hole
- ☐ Musical note
- ☐ Oversized tie
- ☐ Pilgrim hat
- ☐ Police dogs (2)
- ☐ Space dog
- ☐ Stamp
- ☐ Stars (20)
- ☐ Stool
- ☐ Target
- ☐ Top hat
- ☐ Umpire
- ☐ "Unidog"

Hunt for Hector at Dog School and...

- [ ] "Barking King I"
- [ ] Briefcases (3)
- [ ] Canes (2)
- [ ] Cat litter
- [ ] Crown
- [ ] Crying dog
- [ ] "Dog Days"
- [ ] "Doggy Decimal System"
- [ ] "Dog Tail"
- [ ] Easel
- [ ] Empty dog bowls (14)
- [ ] Eraser
- [ ] Fire hydrant
- [ ] Graduate's hat
- [ ] Hammer
- [ ] Ladle
- [ ] Man on leash
- [ ] Napkins (2)
- [ ] Paintbrush
- [ ] Pearl necklace
- [ ] Roller skates
- [ ] Ruler
- [ ] Screwdriver
- [ ] Sleeping dog
- [ ] Spoons (3)
- [ ] Stool
- [ ] Straw
- [ ] "Super Dog"
- [ ] Test tubes (4)

Hunt for Hector among the Dogcatchers and...

- [ ] Airplane
- [ ] Barber pole
- [ ] Bathing dog
- [ ] Briefcase
- [ ] Car antenna
- [ ] Cats (5)
- [ ] Convertible car
- [ ] Dog bowls (3)
- [ ] "Dog mail"
- [ ] Dollar signs (11)
- [ ] Empty bowls (2)
- [ ] Fire hose
- [ ] Fire hydrants (4)
- [ ] Fire truck
- [ ] Fishing pole
- [ ] Guitar
- [ ] Heart
- [ ] Manhole
- [ ] Musical note
- [ ] Net
- [ ] Piano
- [ ] Pink hats (8)
- [ ] Rope swing
- [ ] Satellite dish
- [ ] Shower
- [ ] Sirens (2)
- [ ] Tree
- [ ] Turtle
- [ ] "UDS"
- [ ] Umbrella
- [ ] Watermelon
- [ ] Water tower

Hunt for **Hector**
where the
Rich and Famous
Dogs Live
and...

- ☐ Admiral
- ☐ Alligator
- ☐ Artist
- ☐ "Big Wheel"
- ☐ Bird bath
- ☐ Blimp
- ☐ Bone chimney
- ☐ Candle
- ☐ Castle
- ☐ Cat
- ☐ Cooks (2)
- ☐ Crown
- ☐ Dogfish
- ☐ Dog flag
- ☐ Fire hydrant
- ☐ Golfers (2)
- ☐ Guard
- ☐ Heart
- ☐ Heron
- ☐ Human
- ☐ Joggers (3)
- ☐ Periscope
- ☐ Pillow
- ☐ Pool
- ☐ Sipping a soda
- ☐ Star
- ☐ Tennis player
- ☐ Umbrella
- ☐ Violinist
- ☐ Water-skier
- ☐ Whale

Hunt for Hector at the K-9 Clean up and...

- ☐ Anchor
- ☐ Bones (2)
- ☐ Broken piggy bank
- ☐ Butterfly net
- ☐ Cane
- ☐ Chimney
- ☐ "Chow" bowl
- ☐ Cowboy hat
- ☐ Doorbell
- ☐ Duck
- ☐ Fake mustache
- ☐ Feather
- ☐ Fire hose
- ☐ Fire hydrants (3)
- ☐ Fishing pole
- ☐ Helicopter
- ☐ "K-9" helmet
- ☐ Manhole cover
- ☐ Motorcycle
- ☐ Pails of water (7)
- ☐ Parachute
- ☐ Penguin
- ☐ Rope ladder
- ☐ Rowboat
- ☐ Sailor's hat
- ☐ Scrub brush
- ☐ Skateboard
- ☐ "S.S. Poseidon"
- ☐ Superpooch
- ☐ Tin cans (4)

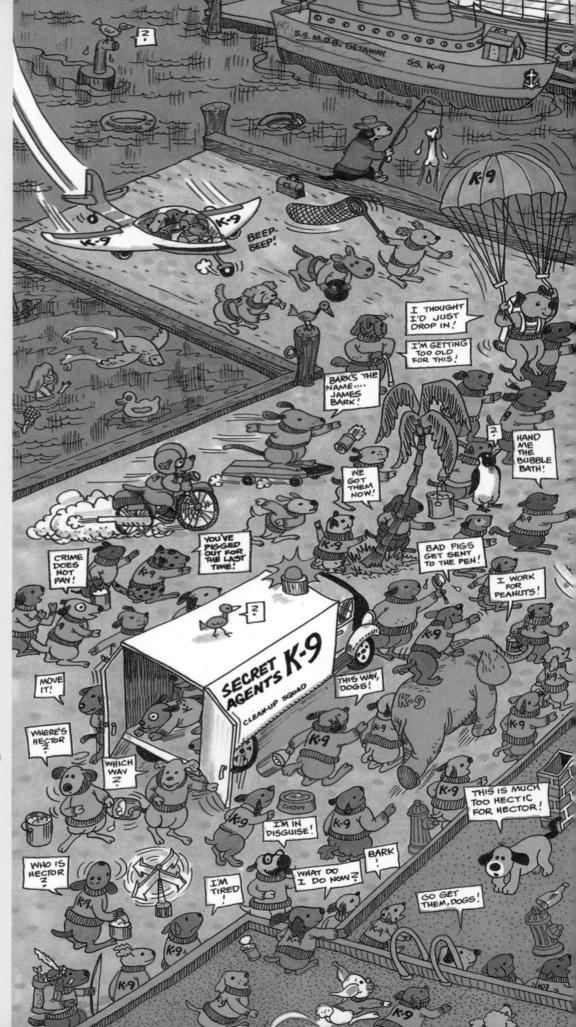

Hunt for Hector at the
Super Dog Bowl
and...

- [ ] "107"
- [ ] Bandaged tail
- [ ] Bench
- [ ] Binoculars
- [ ] Cactus
- [ ] Cracked egg
- [ ] Daisies (3)
- [ ] Dog pile
- [ ] Electrical outlet
- [ ] Footballs (2)
- [ ] Heart-shaped turf
- [ ] Jack-o'-lanterns (5)
- [ ] "Last T.D."
- [ ] Manhole
- [ ] Megaphone
- [ ] Mouse
- [ ] "No Ball Playing"
- [ ] Paint can
- [ ] Patched pants
- [ ] Pirate hat
- [ ] Pom-poms (2)
- [ ] Rabbit
- [ ] Rooster
- [ ] Sleepy dogs (2)
- [ ] Star
- [ ] Sword
- [ ] Target
- [ ] Turtle
- [ ] TV set
- [ ] Water dog
- [ ] Worm

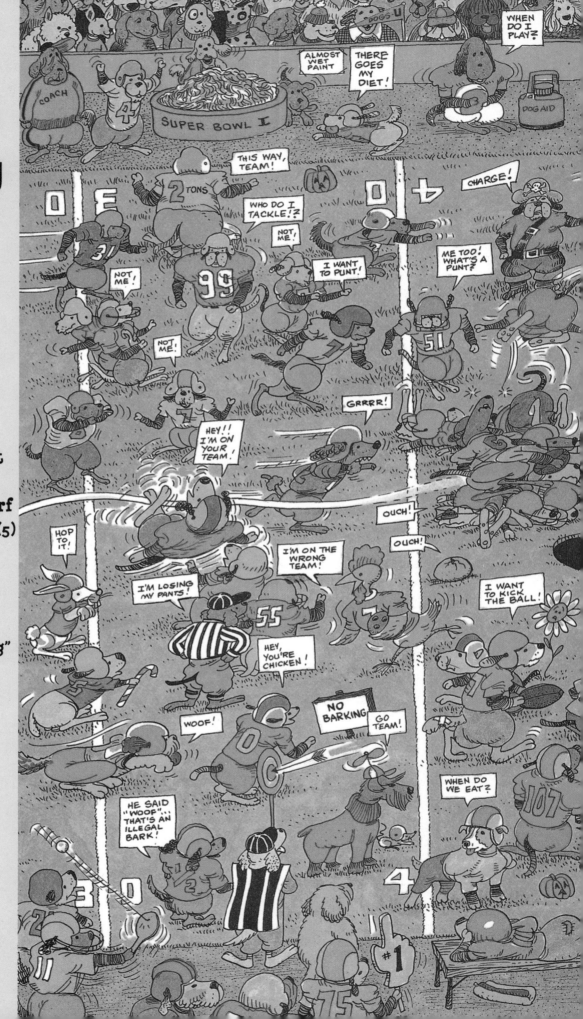

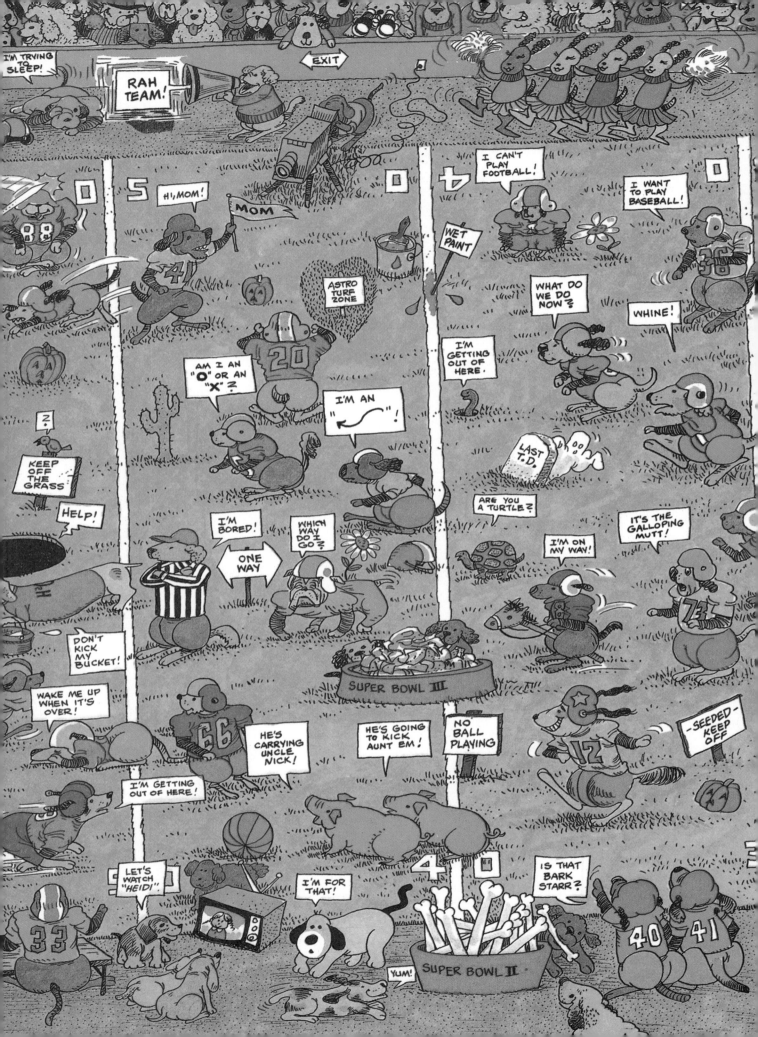

Hunt for Hector
at the
Dog Mall
and...

Hunt for Hector at the
Dog Olympics and...

- ☐ Bone bat
- ☐ Bow
- ☐ Bowling ball
- ☐ Broom
- ☐ Bucket
- ☐ Clipboard
- ☐ Diving board
- ☐ Fallen skater
- ☐ Fencing swords (2)
- ☐ Fishing pole
- ☐ Football players (3)
- ☐ Golf tee
- ☐ Hat with propeller
- ☐ Home plate
- ☐ Ice skates (14)
- ☐ Karate dog
- ☐ Ping-pong paddle
- ☐ Pitcher
- ☐ Pole-vaulter
- ☐ Race car
- ☐ Ski jumper
- ☐ Stop sign
- ☐ Target
- ☐ Tennis racket
- ☐ Top hat
- ☐ Trainer
- ☐ TV camera
- ☐ Volleyball
- ☐ Weight lifter
- ☐ Yo-yo

Hunt for Hector at the TV Quiz Show and...

- ☐ Announcer
- ☐ "Arf TV" (3)
- ☐ Baseball cap
- ☐ Boxes (3)
- ☐ Camera
- ☐ Chef
- ☐ Clipboard
- ☐ Clothespins (2)
- ☐ Coat
- ☐ Contestants (4)
- ☐ Crown
- ☐ Dog collar
- ☐ Dog food
- ☐ Drum
- ☐ "Exit"
- ☐ Flashlight
- ☐ Flowerpot
- ☐ Game wheel
- ☐ Giraffe
- ☐ Gorilla
- ☐ Headphones (5)
- ☐ Magic wand
- ☐ Megaphone
- ☐ Mouse
- ☐ Pencil
- ☐ Pile of bones
- ☐ Space dog
- ☐ Stacks of money (5)
- ☐ Trumpet
- ☐ "V.I.P. Room"

Hunt for Hector
in
Space
and...

- [ ] Bench
- [ ] Blimp
- [ ] Boat
- [ ] Bone antenna
- [ ] Bone smokestack
- [ ] Boxing glove
- [ ] Bus
- [ ] Cars (3)
- [ ] Diving board
- [ ] "Dog fish"
- [ ] Dog in trash can
- [ ] "Dog paddle"
- [ ] Earth
- [ ] Emergency dog
- [ ] Graduate dog
- [ ] Heart with arrow
- [ ] Hot dog
- [ ] Juggler
- [ ] Mailbag
- [ ] Nut
- [ ] Old tire
- [ ] Pirate
- [ ] Pizza
- [ ] Pluto
- [ ] Pup in a cup
- [ ] Roller coaster
- [ ] Space map
- [ ] Star with tail
- [ ] Top hat
- [ ] UFO
- [ ] Unicycle
- [ ] Vampire Dog

Hunt for Hector
in
Dogtown
and...

- [ ] Baby carriage
- [ ] Barbecue
- [ ] "Bark Your Horn"
- [ ] Basketball
- [ ] Bicycle
- [ ] Birds (2)
- [ ] Boat
- [ ] Crossing guard
- [ ] "Dog cookies"
- [ ] Dog fountain
- [ ] Falling "G"
- [ ] Gas pump
- [ ] Hammer
- [ ] Hard hats (3)
- [ ] Human on leash
- [ ] Lawn mower
- [ ] Mailbox
- [ ] Manhole
- [ ] Piano
- [ ] Pool
- [ ] Sailor
- [ ] Santa Claus
- [ ] Screwdriver
- [ ] Skateboard
- [ ] Soccer ball
- [ ] Sock
- [ ] Streetlight
- [ ] Super Dog
- [ ] Swimming pool
- [ ] Trash cans (2)
- [ ] TV
- [ ] Wrench

HUNT FOR HECTOR

SEARCH FOR SAM

FIND FREDDIE

LOOK FOR LISA

LOOK FOR LISA

WHERE ARE THEY?

Look for Lisa in all sorts of crazy places!
While you're looking,
you'll see crazy things, such as:

- Hippos at a rock concert
- Cactuses on the beach
- Parrots in the library
- Surfers on a farm
- Frogs at the flea market
- Snow White at the marathon
- Unicorns in Utah

. . . and much, much more!

Look for Lisa at the Marathon and...

- [ ] Angel
- [ ] Barrel
- [ ] Basketball
- [ ] Bucket
- [ ] Cane
- [ ] Chef
- [ ] Cowboy
- [ ] Deer
- [ ] Diving board
- [ ] Doctor
- [ ] Elephants (2)
- [ ] Ice-cream cone
- [ ] Kite
- [ ] Motorcycle
- [ ] Musical notes (3)
- [ ] Net
- [ ] Octopus
- [ ] Periscope
- [ ] Policeman
- [ ] Rocket
- [ ] Roller skates
- [ ] Sad face
- [ ] Scooter
- [ ] "Shortcut"
- [ ] Sombrero
- [ ] Speed skater
- [ ] Spotted dog
- [ ] Strongman
- [ ] Surfer
- [ ] Taxi
- [ ] Tuba
- [ ] Umbrella

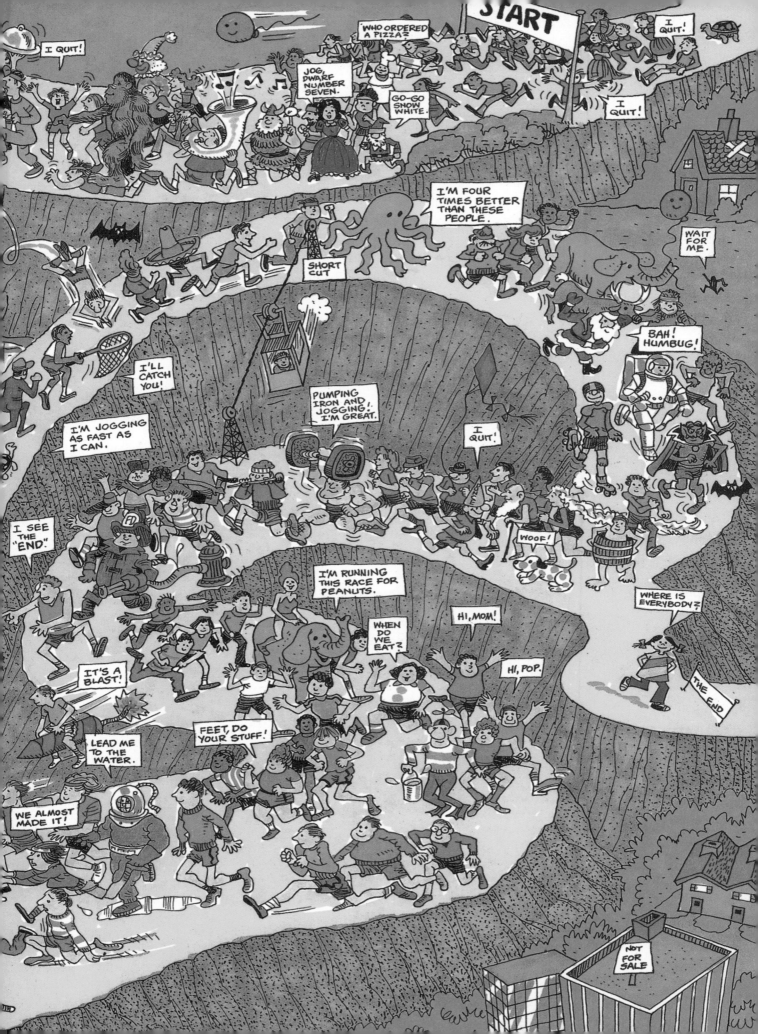

Look for Lisa
After School
and...

- [ ] Balloon
- [ ] Basketballs (2)
- [ ] Baton
- [ ] Bird
- [ ] Camera
- [ ] Chimney
- [ ] Clock faces (2)
- [ ] Donkey
- [ ] Elephant
- [ ] Fish with a hat
- [ ] Flower
- [ ] Grocery cart
- [ ] Hat with propeller
- [ ] Huck Finn
- [ ] Igloo
- [ ] Paper hat
- [ ] Parrot
- [ ] Pencil
- [ ] Pig
- [ ] Plane
- [ ] Rabbit
- [ ] Robot
- [ ] Sailor
- [ ] Ski jumper
- [ ] Smelly potion
- [ ] Snowman
- [ ] Stool
- [ ] Sunglasses
- [ ] Turtle
- [ ] Unicorn
- [ ] Viking helmet

Look for Lisa at the Rock Concert and...

- ☐ Alien
- ☐ Balloons (6)
- ☐ Barbell
- ☐ Bowling ball
- ☐ Crown
- ☐ Doctor
- ☐ Fish tank
- ☐ Flamingo
- ☐ Flowers
- ☐ Hot-dog stand
- ☐ Knight
- ☐ Lamppost
- ☐ Masked man
- ☐ Moon
- ☐ Mummy
- ☐ Net
- ☐ Painter
- ☐ Prisoner
- ☐ Rabbit
- ☐ Snowman
- ☐ Stack of pizza boxes
- ☐ Stars (6)
- ☐ Tin man
- ☐ Tombstones (2)
- ☐ Trampoline
- ☐ Viking
- ☐ Waiter
- ☐ Witch
- ☐ Zebra

Look for Lisa on the Farm and...

- ☐ Cactus
- ☐ Cave
- ☐ Clouds (3)
- ☐ Donkey
- ☐ "Don't Stop" sign
- ☐ Egg
- ☐ Elephant
- ☐ Eskimo
- ☐ Finish line
- ☐ Fox
- ☐ Ghost
- ☐ Giant pumpkin
- ☐ "Grade A"
- ☐ Horses (3)
- ☐ Lion
- ☐ Log pile
- ☐ Message in a bottle
- ☐ Net
- ☐ Periscope
- ☐ Pitchfork
- ☐ Policeman
- ☐ Prisoner
- ☐ Rowboat
- ☐ Scuba diver
- ☐ Stop sign
- ☐ "Summer"
- ☐ Surfboards (2)
- ☐ Tent
- ☐ Turkey
- ☐ Water bucket
- ☐ Weather vane

Look for **Lisa** at the **Beach** and...

- [ ] Artist
- [ ] Beach ball
- [ ] Broom
- [ ] Bunch of balloons
- [ ] Cactus (4)
- [ ] Castle
- [ ] Cello
- [ ] Crocodile
- [ ] Cruise ship
- [ ] Diving board
- [ ] Hearts (3)
- [ ] Horse
- [ ] Jack-in-the-box
- [ ] Kite
- [ ] Lifeguard
- [ ] Lost swim trunks
- [ ] Magnifying glass
- [ ] Merman
- [ ] Palm trees (3)
- [ ] Pickle barrel
- [ ] Policeman
- [ ] Sailboat
- [ ] Sailors (2)
- [ ] Sea serpent
- [ ] Seahorse
- [ ] Starfish (9)
- [ ] Swans (2)
- [ ] Telescope
- [ ] Trash can
- [ ] Tricycle
- [ ] Turtle
- [ ] Whale

Look for Lisa at the Big Sale and...

- ☐ Balloon
- ☐ Clothespins (9)
- ☐ Count Dracula
- ☐ Disappearing men (2)
- ☐ "Don't Stop Shopping"
- ☐ Flower hat
- ☐ Football
- ☐ Football helmet
- ☐ Gumball machine
- ☐ Hard hat
- ☐ Janitor
- ☐ Kite
- ☐ Magic mirror
- ☐ Manhole cover
- ☐ Octopus
- ☐ Paint can
- ☐ Paper airplane
- ☐ Pig
- ☐ Pogo stick
- ☐ Polka-dot shorts
- ☐ Rabbit
- ☐ Rain slicker
- ☐ Rat
- ☐ Robot
- ☐ Roller skates
- ☐ Shirtless shopper
- ☐ Ski jump
- ☐ Skis (8)
- ☐ Teddy bear
- ☐ Turtle

Look for Lisa in the Ocean and...

- ☐ Baby
- ☐ Barrel
- ☐ Baseball bat
- ☐ Basketball
- ☐ Boot
- ☐ Bucket
- ☐ Captain's hat
- ☐ Elephant
- ☐ Fish (3)
- ☐ Guitar
- ☐ Harp
- ☐ Heart
- ☐ Homework
- ☐ Hot-air balloon
- ☐ Ice-cream cone
- ☐ Key
- ☐ Oars (5)
- ☐ Painting
- ☐ Palm tree
- ☐ Scuba diver
- ☐ Shark fins (2)
- ☐ Slice of watermelon
- ☐ Sock
- ☐ Surfer
- ☐ Television
- ☐ Tin can
- ☐ Tire
- ☐ Tree

Look for **Lisa** at the **Library** and...

- [ ] Baseball
- [ ] Birdcage
- [ ] Bowling pins (10)
- [ ] Brooms (2)
- [ ] Cactus
- [ ] Cactus book
- [ ] Cake
- [ ] Campfire
- [ ] Candle
- [ ] Car
- [ ] Football player
- [ ] Frying pan
- [ ] Globe
- [ ] Hamburger
- [ ] Hearts (4)
- [ ] Hockey stick
- [ ] Hot dog
- [ ] Jack-in-the-box
- [ ] Knight
- [ ] Monster hands (3)
- [ ] Musical note
- [ ] Napoleon
- [ ] Old tire
- [ ] Pole-vaulter
- [ ] Policewoman
- [ ] "Quiet" signs (6)
- [ ] Smiley face
- [ ] Teapot
- [ ] Trapdoor
- [ ] Tricycle
- [ ] Wagon
- [ ] Witch

Look for **Lisa** at the
Amusement
Park
and...

- ☐ All-north weather vane
- ☐ Archer
- ☐ Cheese
- ☐ Clock
- ☐ Clowns (3)
- ☐ Cowboys (2)
- ☐ Crocodile
- ☐ Crooked chimney
- ☐ Diving board
- ☐ Dollar sign
- ☐ Fishing pole
- ☐ Heads without bodies (2)
- ☐ Ice block
- ☐ Manhole
- ☐ Moon
- ☐ Mouse hole
- ☐ Mummy
- ☐ Pear
- ☐ Snowman
- ☐ Space explorer
- ☐ Tent
- ☐ Tied-up man
- ☐ Tin man
- ☐ Tombstones (3)
- ☐ "Tunnel of Love"
- ☐ Umbrella
- ☐ Witch
- ☐ Wristwatches (7)

Look for Lisa at the Flea Market and...

Look for Lisa as the Circus Comes to Town and...

- [ ] Aliens (2)
- [ ] Barbell
- [ ] Bass drum
- [ ] Bone
- [ ] Broom
- [ ] Camel
- [ ] Cowboys (4)
- [ ] Crown
- [ ] "Enter"
- [ ] Flags (7)
- [ ] Frankenstein's monster
- [ ] Hole
- [ ] Juggler
- [ ] Musical note
- [ ] Net
- [ ] Plates (7)
- [ ] Police officers (2)
- [ ] Poodle
- [ ] Rabbit
- [ ] Sad face
- [ ] Soldiers (2)
- [ ] Stroller
- [ ] Tin man
- [ ] Turtle
- [ ] Unicorn
- [ ] Unicycle
- [ ] Whistle
- [ ] Witch

LOOK FOR LISA   **FIND FREDDIE**   **SEARCH FOR SAM**   **HUNT FOR HECTOR**

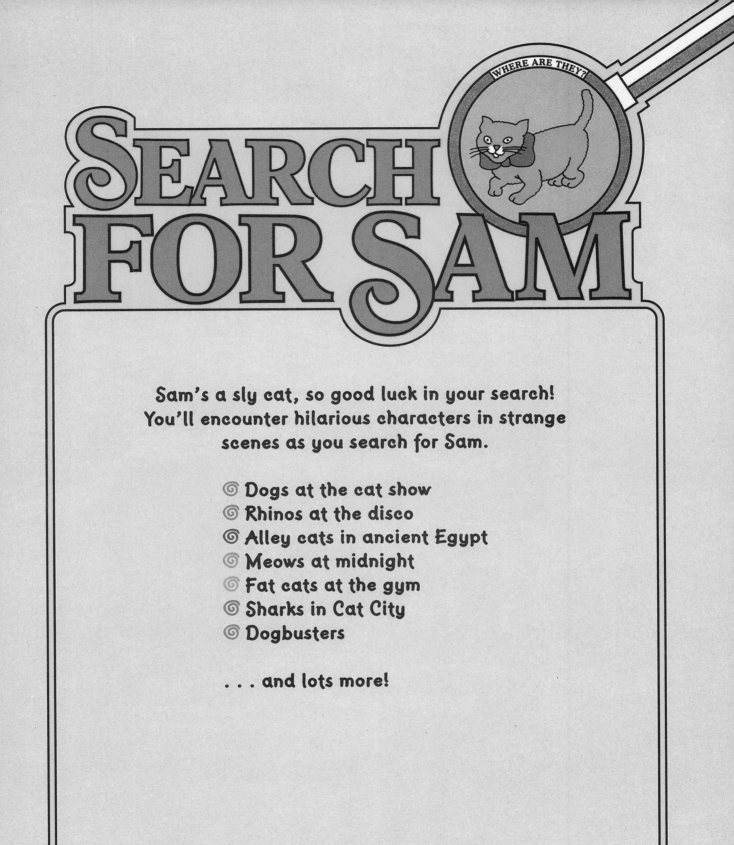

SEARCH FOR SAM

WHERE ARE THEY?

Sam's a sly cat, so good luck in your search!
You'll encounter hilarious characters in strange
scenes as you search for Sam.

- Dogs at the cat show
- Rhinos at the disco
- Alley cats in ancient Egypt
- Meows at midnight
- Fat cats at the gym
- Sharks in Cat City
- Dogbusters

. . . and lots more!

Search for Sam in Cat City and...

- [ ] Airplane
- [ ] Antenna
- [ ] Balloons (2)
- [ ] Barrel
- [ ] Blimp
- [ ] Candle
- [ ] Cracked window
- [ ] Elephant
- [ ] Fire hydrant
- [ ] Flowerpot
- [ ] Fur coat
- [ ] Hammer
- [ ] Hard hats (3)
- [ ] Mailbox
- [ ] Manhole cover
- [ ] Motorcycle
- [ ] Musical notes (8)
- [ ] Octopus
- [ ] Piano
- [ ] Red bow
- [ ] Rocket
- [ ] Rooster
- [ ] Scarf
- [ ] Sharks (3)
- [ ] Shovel
- [ ] Sock
- [ ] Sun
- [ ] Telephone booth
- [ ] Toolbox
- [ ] Towel
- [ ] Turtle
- [ ] Waiter

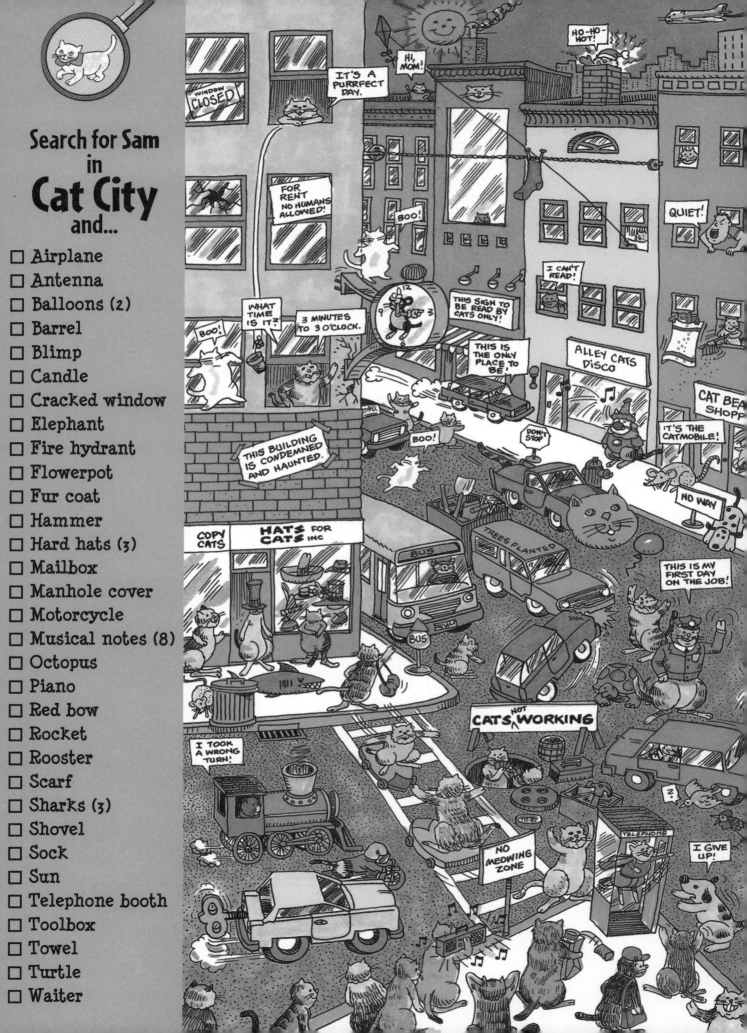

Search for **Sam** on **Friday the 13th** and...

- ☐ Black cats (4)
- ☐ Bow tie
- ☐ Candy cane
- ☐ Clock
- ☐ Clothesline
- ☐ Count Dracula
- ☐ Count Dracula Jr.
- ☐ Cow
- ☐ Cracked mirror
- ☐ Doctor
- ☐ Eye patch
- ☐ Fish
- ☐ Flying witch
- ☐ Football
- ☐ Headless man
- ☐ Head looking for body
- ☐ Horse and carriage
- ☐ Kite
- ☐ Magic carpet
- ☐ One-eyed monsters (2)
- ☐ Painter
- ☐ Pig
- ☐ Quicksand
- ☐ Rabbit
- ☐ Sailboat
- ☐ Turtle
- ☐ Two-faced man
- ☐ Wooden leg

Search for Sam at Fat Cat Gym and...

- ☐ Book
- ☐ Bowling ball
- ☐ Breaking rope
- ☐ Burned feet
- ☐ Cat food dish
- ☐ Catnap
- ☐ Clipboard
- ☐ Cool cat
- ☐ Dog bone
- ☐ "Do Not Touch"
- ☐ Escaped bird
- ☐ Fish (2)
- ☐ Fishbowl
- ☐ Fish skeletons (6)
- ☐ Hearts (3)
- ☐ Helmet
- ☐ Ice-cream cones (2)
- ☐ Jump rope
- ☐ Money
- ☐ Pair of boxing gloves
- ☐ Pizza
- ☐ Prisoner
- ☐ Punching bags (2)
- ☐ Rats (3)
- ☐ Stationary bike
- ☐ Sweatbands (13)
- ☐ Tail warmer
- ☐ Torn pants
- ☐ Window
- ☐ Yoga mats (3)

Search for Sam at the
Midnight Meowing
and...

- [ ] Baseball
- [ ] Baseball bat
- [ ] Birdhouse
- [ ] Can
- [ ] Cannon
- [ ] Cloud
- [ ] Egg
- [ ] Fishbowl
- [ ] Fish skeletons (2)
- [ ] Football
- [ ] Gate
- [ ] Jack-o'-lantern
- [ ] Light
- [ ] Microphone
- [ ] Moon
- [ ] "No Welcome" mat
- [ ] Old tire
- [ ] Piggy bank
- [ ] Police car
- [ ] Policeman
- [ ] Pot
- [ ] Record player
- [ ] Rolling pin
- [ ] Spoon
- [ ] Stacks of paper (2)
- [ ] Stars (4)
- [ ] Table
- [ ] Tent
- [ ] UFO
- [ ] Wood planks (3)
- [ ] Yo-yo

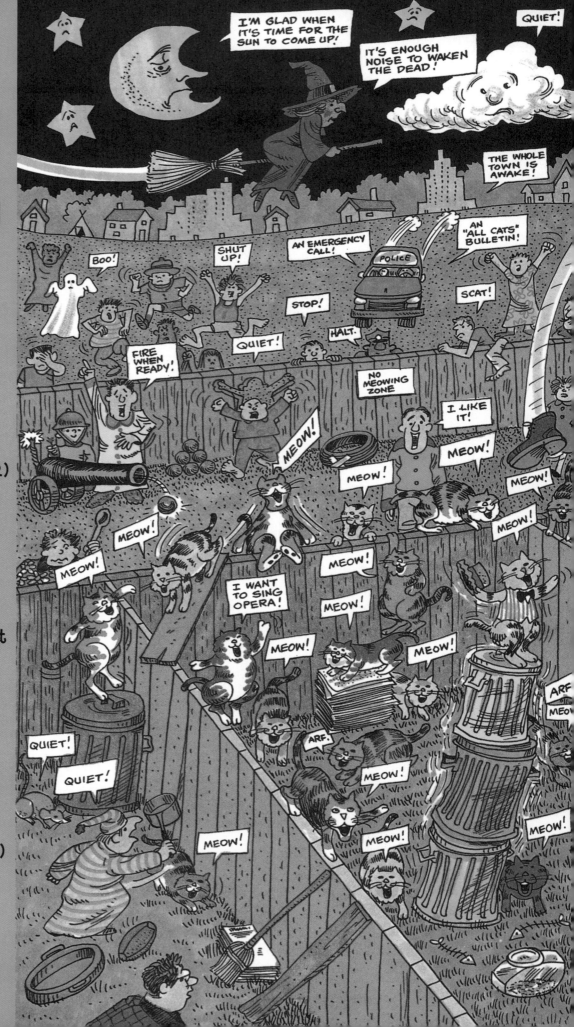

Search for Sam at the **Disco** and...

- [ ] Ballerina
- [ ] Blue rhinos (2)
- [ ] Cat blowing horn
- [ ] Cat break-dancing
- [ ] Chef
- [ ] Clipboard
- [ ] Clown cat
- [ ] Cowboy cat
- [ ] Disco ball
- [ ] Doctor
- [ ] Dog
- [ ] Duck
- [ ] Earplug seller
- [ ] Earrings
- [ ] Eye patch
- [ ] Flowerpot
- [ ] Hard hat
- [ ] Karate cat
- [ ] Lampshade
- [ ] Pig
- [ ] Pirate sword
- [ ] Pizza
- [ ] Police officer
- [ ] Record player
- [ ] Roller skates
- [ ] Skis
- [ ] Snowcat
- [ ] Speakers (10)
- [ ] Sunglasses
- [ ] Swinging cat
- [ ] Top hat
- [ ] Wooden leg

Search for Sam in
Ancient Egypt
and...

- ☐ Antenna
- ☐ Arrows (4)
- ☐ Boats (2)
- ☐ Boxes (3)
- ☐ Bucket
- ☐ Cats in bikinis (2)
- ☐ Falling coconuts (2)
- ☐ Fan
- ☐ Fire
- ☐ Fishing poles (2)
- ☐ Flying carpet
- ☐ Guard cats (5)
- ☐ Hippo
- ☐ Horse
- ☐ Jester
- ☐ Mummies (2)
- ☐ Palm trees (2)
- ☐ Pyramids (8)
- ☐ Quicksand
- ☐ Red birds (4)
- ☐ Red bow
- ☐ Rolled paper
- ☐ Sand pail
- ☐ Shovel
- ☐ Smiley face
- ☐ Snakes (2)
- ☐ Snowman
- ☐ Taxi
- ☐ Telephone
- ☐ Umbrella

Search for **Sam** at the **Cat Show** and...

- ☐ Ball of yarn
- ☐ Banjo
- ☐ Beach chair
- ☐ Bib
- ☐ Bones (2)
- ☐ Broom
- ☐ Camera
- ☐ Coconuts (2)
- ☐ Cow
- ☐ Cracked wall
- ☐ Cymbals (2)
- ☐ Fish bones (4)
- ☐ Fishing pole
- ☐ Graduate
- ☐ Guitar
- ☐ Hearts (3)
- ☐ Joggers (2)
- ☐ Lion
- ☐ Man in a cat suit
- ☐ Net
- ☐ Newspaper
- ☐ Palm tree
- ☐ Pizza boxes (2)
- ☐ Pool
- ☐ Scarf
- ☐ Sombrero
- ☐ Red bow
- ☐ Red curtain
- ☐ Royal cat
- ☐ Ticket booth
- ☐ Tombstone
- ☐ Witch

Search for Sam with the
Dogbusters
and...

- [ ] Balloon
- [ ] Birdhouse
- [ ] Bones (13)
- [ ] Bridge
- [ ] Broom
- [ ] Clown
- [ ] Crane
- [ ] Crocodile
- [ ] Detective
- [ ] Dogs in tree (2)
- [ ] Fish (4)
- [ ] Flag
- [ ] Flower
- [ ] Hollow log
- [ ] Horse
- [ ] Jack-o'-lantern
- [ ] Ladders (3)
- [ ] Lamppost
- [ ] Manhole cover
- [ ] Old tire
- [ ] Pizza box
- [ ] Saddle
- [ ] Sailboat
- [ ] Siren
- [ ] Surfboard
- [ ] Taxi
- [ ] Tent
- [ ] Tightrope walker
- [ ] Turtle
- [ ] Umbrella
- [ ] Wanted poster
- [ ] Witch

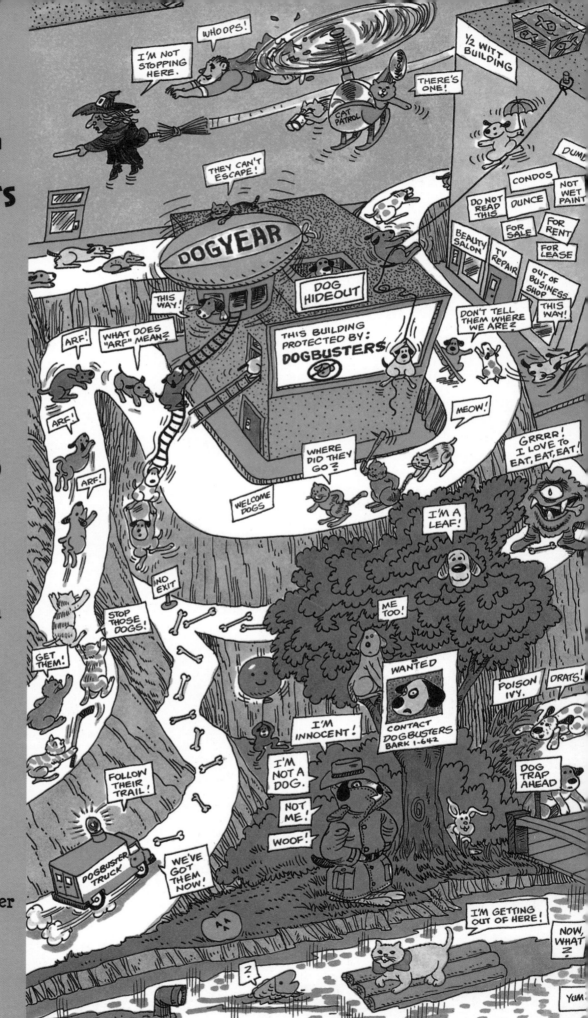

Search for Sam at the North Pole and...

- ☐ Badge
- ☐ Bells (2)
- ☐ Bread
- ☐ Broken chair
- ☐ Cactus
- ☐ Campfire
- ☐ Chef's hat
- ☐ Clock
- ☐ Fish
- ☐ Fishing pole
- ☐ Football
- ☐ Globe
- ☐ Green sock
- ☐ Hammer
- ☐ Kite
- ☐ Locomotive
- ☐ Miner's hat
- ☐ Musical notes (3)
- ☐ Ornament
- ☐ Pizza
- ☐ Polar bear
- ☐ Reindeer
- ☐ Satellite dish
- ☐ Singing birds (2)
- ☐ Skier
- ☐ Snake with a hat
- ☐ Stepladder
- ☐ Toy car
- ☐ Yo-yo
- ☐ Zebras (2)

SEARCH FOR SAM FIND FREDDIE HUNT FOR HECTOR LOOK FOR LISA

DETECT DONALD

Detect Donald at the Cheez-E Diner and...

- [ ] Bear
- [ ] Bowling ball
- [ ] Dinosaur
- [ ] Dog
- [ ] Ear of corn
- [ ] Earrings (3)
- [ ] Elf
- [ ] Eye patch
- [ ] Frankenstein's monster
- [ ] Ghost
- [ ] King
- [ ] Knight in armor
- [ ] Leaf
- [ ] Menus (2)
- [ ] Parrot
- [ ] Pot
- [ ] Raccoon hat
- [ ] Sailor hat
- [ ] Shark
- [ ] Skeleton
- [ ] Slice of watermelon
- [ ] Snake
- [ ] Straw
- [ ] Sunglasses (2)
- [ ] Watch

- ☐ Antenna
- ☐ Baseball
- ☐ Basket
- ☐ Bell
- ☐ Ben Franklin
- ☐ Betsy Ross
- ☐ Bone
- ☐ Broom
- ☐ Bucket
- ☐ Candles (2)
- ☐ Cannonballs (4)
- ☐ Cats (2)
- ☐ Chicken
- ☐ Clock
- ☐ Dogs (2)
- ☐ Drums (3)
- ☐ Duck
- ☐ Ear of corn
- ☐ Flower vase
- ☐ Horses (4)
- ☐ Kites (2)
- ☐ Lamppost
- ☐ Mouse
- ☐ One dollar bill
- ☐ Saw
- ☐ Spinning wheel

Detect Donald in the **Middle Ages** and...

- [ ] Animal horns (2)
- [ ] Axe
- [ ] Baseball caps (2)
- [ ] Bird
- [ ] Candles (3)
- [ ] Clothespin
- [ ] Crutch
- [ ] Donkey
- [ ] Dragon
- [ ] Duck
- [ ] Fan
- [ ] Fish
- [ ] Flags (5)
- [ ] Hat feathers (4)
- [ ] Helmet with horns
- [ ] Lances (3)
- [ ] Mouse
- [ ] Propeller
- [ ] Queen
- [ ] Red bows (2)
- [ ] Sergeant's stripes
- [ ] Stars (2)
- [ ] Sunglasses (2)
- [ ] Tombstone
- [ ] UFO
- [ ] Weather vane

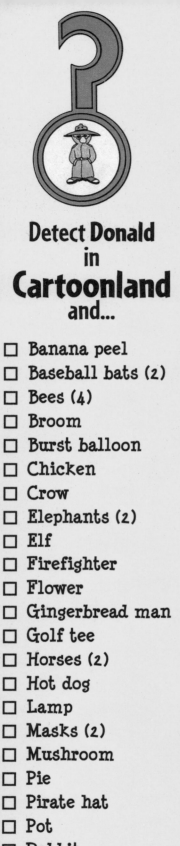

Detect Donald in Cartoonland and...

- ☐ Banana peel
- ☐ Baseball bats (2)
- ☐ Bees (4)
- ☐ Broom
- ☐ Burst balloon
- ☐ Chicken
- ☐ Crow
- ☐ Elephants (2)
- ☐ Elf
- ☐ Firefighter
- ☐ Flower
- ☐ Gingerbread man
- ☐ Golf tee
- ☐ Horses (2)
- ☐ Hot dog
- ☐ Lamp
- ☐ Masks (2)
- ☐ Mushroom
- ☐ Pie
- ☐ Pirate hat
- ☐ Pot
- ☐ Rabbit
- ☐ Sandwich
- ☐ Saxophone
- ☐ Scarf
- ☐ Snake
- ☐ Swiss cheese
- ☐ Underwear

Detect Donald at the Pirates' Battle and...

Detect Donald
in the
Future
and...

- ☐ Apple
- ☐ Cactus
- ☐ Christmas ornament
- ☐ Clock
- ☐ Ear
- ☐ Elephant
- ☐ Evergreen tree
- ☐ Fish
- ☐ Football
- ☐ Football helmet
- ☐ Graduate's hat
- ☐ Guitar
- ☐ Ice-cream cone
- ☐ Ice skate
- ☐ Jester
- ☐ Key
- ☐ Nail
- ☐ Paintbrush
- ☐ Postage stamp
- ☐ Roller skate
- ☐ Santa Claus
- ☐ Skateboard
- ☐ Snowman
- ☐ Spoon
- ☐ Stop sign
- ☐ Tepee
- ☐ Watering can

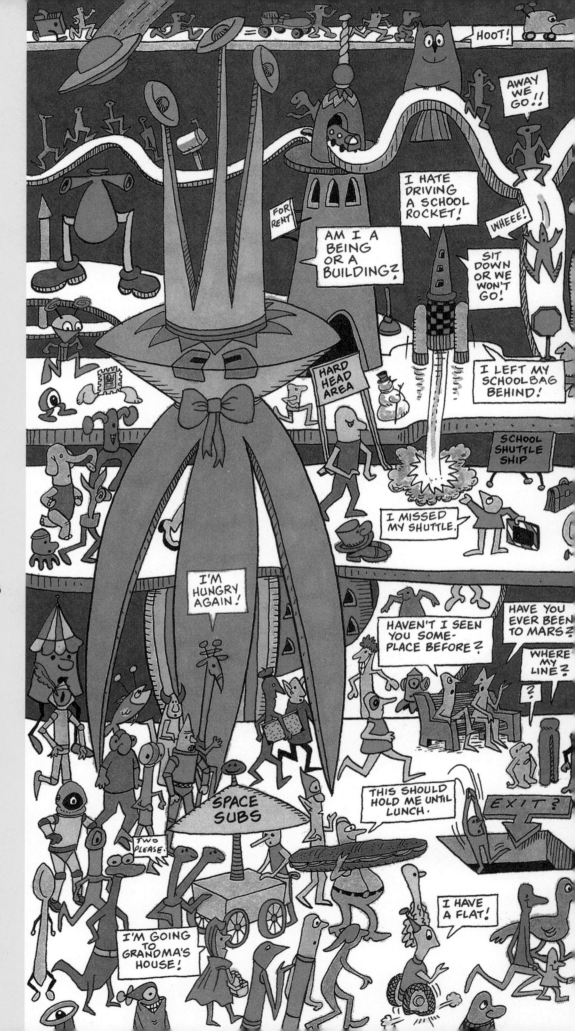

Detect **Donald**
in
Napoleon's France
and...

- [ ] Alien
- [ ] Arrow
- [ ] Basket
- [ ] Basketball players (2)
- [ ] Baton twirler
- [ ] Bear
- [ ] Bowling ball
- [ ] Crown
- [ ] Fishing pole
- [ ] French bread
- [ ] Garbage can
- [ ] Haystack
- [ ] Ice-cream cone
- [ ] Jack-o'-lantern
- [ ] Key
- [ ] Lost boot
- [ ] Mask
- [ ] Mermaid
- [ ] Mouse
- [ ] Net
- [ ] Paintbrush
- [ ] Propeller
- [ ] Red bird
- [ ] Rooster
- [ ] Skull
- [ ] Tin can
- [ ] Turtle
- [ ] Watering can
- [ ] Witch

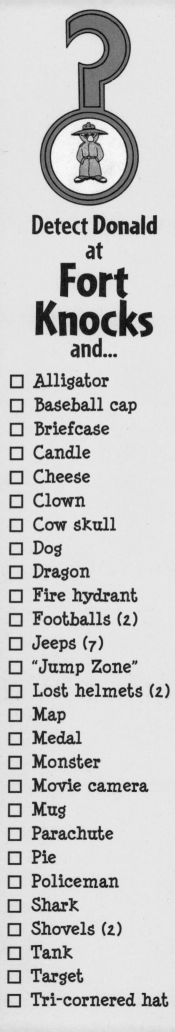

Detect Donald at
Fort Knocks
and...

- ☐ Alligator
- ☐ Baseball cap
- ☐ Briefcase
- ☐ Candle
- ☐ Cheese
- ☐ Clown
- ☐ Cow skull
- ☐ Dog
- ☐ Dragon
- ☐ Fire hydrant
- ☐ Footballs (2)
- ☐ Jeeps (7)
- ☐ "Jump Zone"
- ☐ Lost helmets (2)
- ☐ Map
- ☐ Medal
- ☐ Monster
- ☐ Movie camera
- ☐ Mug
- ☐ Parachute
- ☐ Pie
- ☐ Policeman
- ☐ Shark
- ☐ Shovels (2)
- ☐ Tank
- ☐ Target
- ☐ Tri-cornered hat

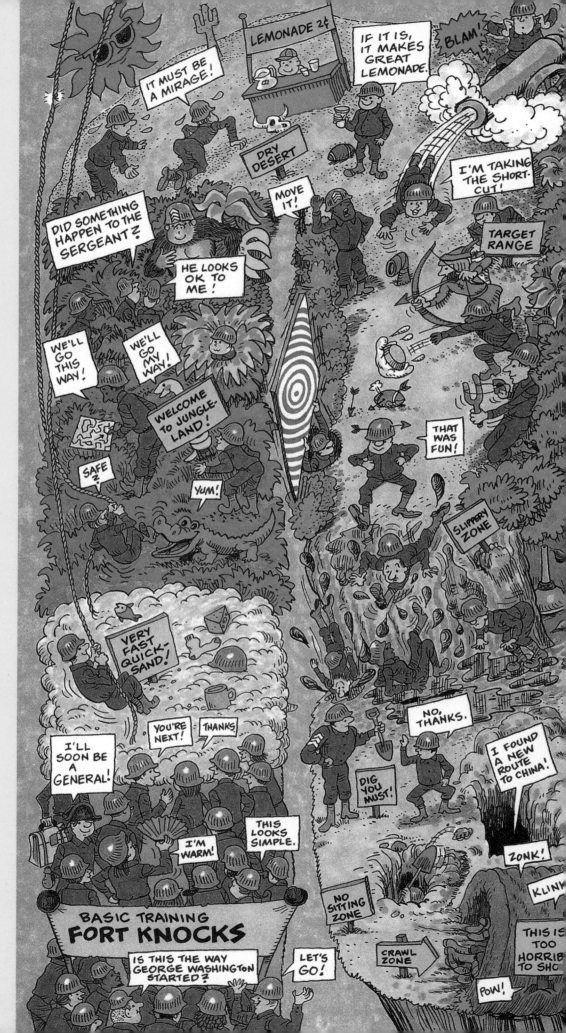

Detect Donald in Ancient Rome

and...

- ☐ Arrow
- ☐ Backwards helmet
- ☐ Balloon
- ☐ Cactus
- ☐ Caesar
- ☐ Cat
- ☐ Falling rock
- ☐ Flower
- ☐ Horseless chariot
- ☐ Jack-o'-lantern
- ☐ Julius and Augustus
- ☐ Kite
- ☐ Mask
- ☐ Painted egg
- ☐ Pig
- ☐ Pizza box
- ☐ Puddles (2)
- ☐ Rabbit
- ☐ Shield
- ☐ Skull
- ☐ Slice of pizza
- ☐ Snake
- ☐ Sock
- ☐ Spears (2)
- ☐ Star
- ☐ Underwear

Detect Donald
in
Prehistoric Times
and...

- [ ] Blue hats (3)
- [ ] Briefcase
- [ ] Broom
- [ ] Car
- [ ] Cave
- [ ] Crown
- [ ] Football
- [ ] Glass pitcher
- [ ] Guitar
- [ ] Kite
- [ ] Lasso
- [ ] Lion
- [ ] Logs (2)
- [ ] Lunch box
- [ ] Periscope
- [ ] Pig
- [ ] Pink flamingo
- [ ] Red bows (4)
- [ ] Snakes (3)
- [ ] Soccer ball
- [ ] Spoon
- [ ] Stone axe
- [ ] Superhero
- [ ] Tin man
- [ ] Tire
- [ ] Trumpet
- [ ] Volcano

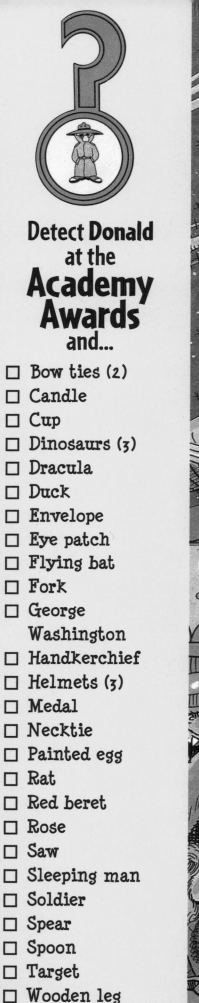

Detect Donald at the Academy Awards and...

- ☐ Bow ties (2)
- ☐ Candle
- ☐ Cup
- ☐ Dinosaurs (3)
- ☐ Dracula
- ☐ Duck
- ☐ Envelope
- ☐ Eye patch
- ☐ Flying bat
- ☐ Fork
- ☐ George Washington
- ☐ Handkerchief
- ☐ Helmets (3)
- ☐ Medal
- ☐ Necktie
- ☐ Painted egg
- ☐ Rat
- ☐ Red beret
- ☐ Rose
- ☐ Saw
- ☐ Sleeping man
- ☐ Soldier
- ☐ Spear
- ☐ Spoon
- ☐ Target
- ☐ Wooden leg

LOOK FOR LAURA

DETECT DONALD

FIND FRANKIE

SEARCH FOR SUSIE

FIND FRANKIE

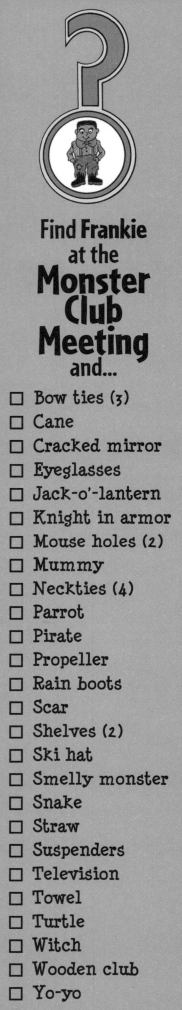

Find **Frankie** at the **Monster Club Meeting** and...

- ☐ Bow ties (3)
- ☐ Cane
- ☐ Cracked mirror
- ☐ Eyeglasses
- ☐ Jack-o'-lantern
- ☐ Knight in armor
- ☐ Mouse holes (2)
- ☐ Mummy
- ☐ Neckties (4)
- ☐ Parrot
- ☐ Pirate
- ☐ Propeller
- ☐ Rain boots
- ☐ Scar
- ☐ Shelves (2)
- ☐ Ski hat
- ☐ Smelly monster
- ☐ Snake
- ☐ Straw
- ☐ Suspenders
- ☐ Television
- ☐ Towel
- ☐ Turtle
- ☐ Witch
- ☐ Wooden club
- ☐ Yo-yo

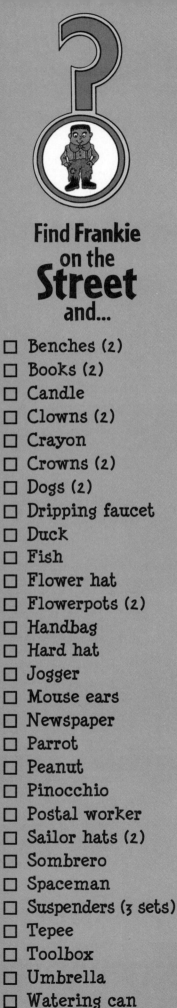

Find Frankie in the **Supermarket** and...

- ☐ Bandannas (3)
- ☐ Bare foot
- ☐ Broom
- ☐ Cobweb
- ☐ Cook
- ☐ Cowboy
- ☐ Crown
- ☐ Dogfish
- ☐ Eggs
- ☐ Firefighter
- ☐ Fire hydrant
- ☐ Fishing pole
- ☐ Football player
- ☐ Handbag
- ☐ Jack-in-the-box
- ☐ Knee pads
- ☐ Paddles (2)
- ☐ Pear
- ☐ People sleeping (2)
- ☐ Pocket watch
- ☐ Pole-vaulter
- ☐ Propeller
- ☐ Scarves (2)
- ☐ Snake
- ☐ Straw
- ☐ Sunglasses
- ☐ Swordfish
- ☐ Toaster
- ☐ TV camera
- ☐ TV set
- ☐ Worms (2)

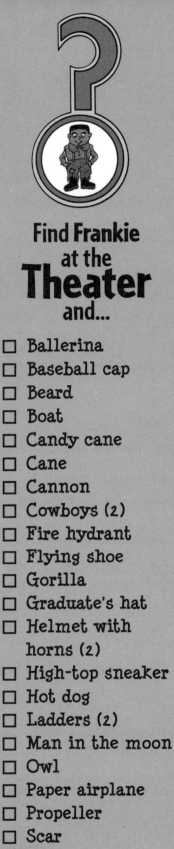

Find Frankie at the **Theater** and...

- ☐ Ballerina
- ☐ Baseball cap
- ☐ Beard
- ☐ Boat
- ☐ Candy cane
- ☐ Cane
- ☐ Cannon
- ☐ Cowboys (2)
- ☐ Fire hydrant
- ☐ Flying shoe
- ☐ Gorilla
- ☐ Graduate's hat
- ☐ Helmet with horns (2)
- ☐ High-top sneaker
- ☐ Hot dog
- ☐ Ladders (2)
- ☐ Man in the moon
- ☐ Owl
- ☐ Paper airplane
- ☐ Propeller
- ☐ Scar
- ☐ Sheep
- ☐ Skull
- ☐ Suspenders (2 pairs)
- ☐ Target
- ☐ Tent
- ☐ Trapeze artist
- ☐ Underwear

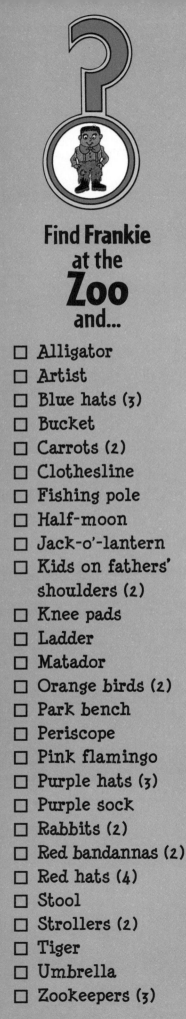

Find Frankie at the Zoo and...

- [ ] Alligator
- [ ] Artist
- [ ] Blue hats (3)
- [ ] Bucket
- [ ] Carrots (2)
- [ ] Clothesline
- [ ] Fishing pole
- [ ] Half-moon
- [ ] Jack-o'-lantern
- [ ] Kids on fathers' shoulders (2)
- [ ] Knee pads
- [ ] Ladder
- [ ] Matador
- [ ] Orange birds (2)
- [ ] Park bench
- [ ] Periscope
- [ ] Pink flamingo
- [ ] Purple hats (3)
- [ ] Purple sock
- [ ] Rabbits (2)
- [ ] Red bandannas (2)
- [ ] Red hats (4)
- [ ] Stool
- [ ] Strollers (2)
- [ ] Tiger
- [ ] Umbrella
- [ ] Zookeepers (3)

Find Frankie at the Yum-Yum Emporium and...

- ☐ Alien
- ☐ Baseball cap
- ☐ Bib
- ☐ Birdcage
- ☐ Book
- ☐ Booster seat
- ☐ Briefcase
- ☐ Crown
- ☐ Crutch
- ☐ Cupcake
- ☐ Duck
- ☐ Eye patch
- ☐ Food fight
- ☐ Football player
- ☐ Ice-cream cone
- ☐ Mailbox
- ☐ Man with fingers in ears
- ☐ Napkin dispensers (2)
- ☐ Pearl necklaces (2)
- ☐ Pig
- ☐ Pizza
- ☐ Rain slicker
- ☐ Red bandannas (2)
- ☐ Red hats (2)
- ☐ Salt shaker
- ☐ Shark fin
- ☐ Straws (2)
- ☐ Sunglasses (2)
- ☐ Suspenders
- ☐ Volcano

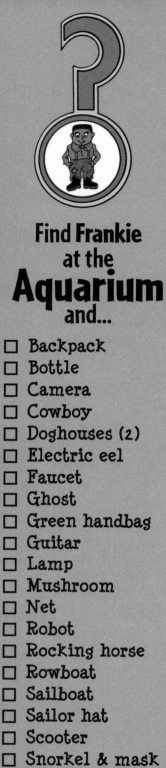

Find Frankie at the Aquarium and...

- ☐ Backpack
- ☐ Bottle
- ☐ Camera
- ☐ Cowboy
- ☐ Doghouses (2)
- ☐ Electric eel
- ☐ Faucet
- ☐ Ghost
- ☐ Green handbag
- ☐ Guitar
- ☐ Lamp
- ☐ Mushroom
- ☐ Net
- ☐ Robot
- ☐ Rocking horse
- ☐ Rowboat
- ☐ Sailboat
- ☐ Sailor hat
- ☐ Scooter
- ☐ Snorkel & mask
- ☐ Snowman
- ☐ Snowshoes
- ☐ Starfish (3)
- ☐ Swords (2)
- ☐ Teacher
- ☐ Telescope
- ☐ Tin man
- ☐ Turtles (3)
- ☐ Whip
- ☐ Witch
- ☐ Wooden bucket

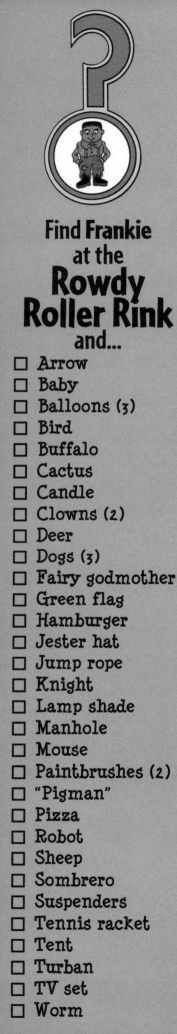

Find Frankie at the Rowdy Roller Rink and...

- ☐ Arrow
- ☐ Baby
- ☐ Balloons (3)
- ☐ Bird
- ☐ Buffalo
- ☐ Cactus
- ☐ Candle
- ☐ Clowns (2)
- ☐ Deer
- ☐ Dogs (3)
- ☐ Fairy godmother
- ☐ Green flag
- ☐ Hamburger
- ☐ Jester hat
- ☐ Jump rope
- ☐ Knight
- ☐ Lamp shade
- ☐ Manhole
- ☐ Mouse
- ☐ Paintbrushes (2)
- ☐ "Pigman"
- ☐ Pizza
- ☐ Robot
- ☐ Sheep
- ☐ Sombrero
- ☐ Suspenders
- ☐ Tennis racket
- ☐ Tent
- ☐ Turban
- ☐ TV set
- ☐ Worm

Find Frankie in the **Arcade** and...

- ☐ Balloon
- ☐ Baseball
- ☐ Beach ball
- ☐ Bees (2)
- ☐ Birdcage
- ☐ Black cat
- ☐ Book
- ☐ Bucket
- ☐ Cannon
- ☐ Dracula
- ☐ Faucet
- ☐ Football
- ☐ Hard hat
- ☐ Jack-o'-lantern
- ☐ Lightning
- ☐ Maze
- ☐ Mouse
- ☐ Mummy
- ☐ Policeman
- ☐ Rocket
- ☐ Sailor hat
- ☐ Stuffed animal
- ☐ Sunglasses
- ☐ Target
- ☐ Top hat
- ☐ Turtle
- ☐ Umbrella
- ☐ Yo-yo

Find Frankie
in the
Suburbs
and...

- [ ] Basketball
- [ ] Bone
- [ ] Books (3)
- [ ] Broken window
- [ ] Broom
- [ ] "Dead End"
- [ ] Flying bat
- [ ] Gate
- [ ] Ghost
- [ ] Golf bag
- [ ] Guitar
- [ ] Hammock
- [ ] Haunted house
- [ ] Jogger
- [ ] Jump rope
- [ ] Mailbox
- [ ] Mail delivery
- [ ] Monster hands (2)
- [ ] Mouse
- [ ] Rabbit
- [ ] Shovel
- [ ] Snake
- [ ] Sunglasses
- [ ] Superhero
- [ ] Tea bag
- [ ] Tire swing
- [ ] Trash cans (3)
- [ ] Tuba
- [ ] TV antenna

Find Frankie at the **Monsters' New Clubhouse** and...

- ☐ Bee
- ☐ Broom
- ☐ Candles (2)
- ☐ Clouds (2)
- ☐ Cobweb
- ☐ Doormat
- ☐ Flower
- ☐ Football
- ☐ Heart
- ☐ Light bulb
- ☐ Mouse hole
- ☐ Mustache
- ☐ Neckties (2)
- ☐ Octopus
- ☐ Pirate
- ☐ Pointed hats (2)
- ☐ Sled
- ☐ Smiling ghosts (2)
- ☐ Smiling star
- ☐ Snake
- ☐ Thirteens (4)
- ☐ Tic-tac-toe
- ☐ Tiny monster
- ☐ Trapdoor
- ☐ Trees (2)
- ☐ Turtle
- ☐ Umbrella
- ☐ Unhappy moon

FIND FRANKIE

SEARCH FOR SUSIE

LOOK FOR LAURA

DETECT DONALD

LOOK FOR LAURA

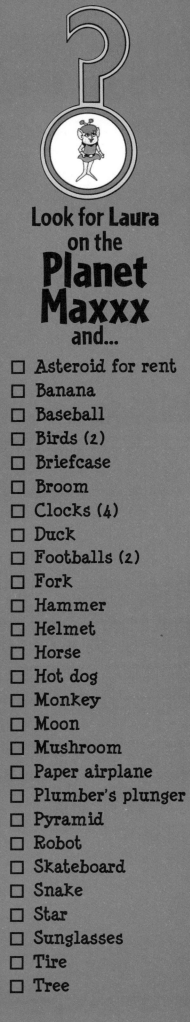

Look for Laura on the
Planet Maxxx
and...

- ☐ Asteroid for rent
- ☐ Banana
- ☐ Baseball
- ☐ Birds (2)
- ☐ Briefcase
- ☐ Broom
- ☐ Clocks (4)
- ☐ Duck
- ☐ Footballs (2)
- ☐ Fork
- ☐ Hammer
- ☐ Helmet
- ☐ Horse
- ☐ Hot dog
- ☐ Monkey
- ☐ Moon
- ☐ Mushroom
- ☐ Paper airplane
- ☐ Plumber's plunger
- ☐ Pyramid
- ☐ Robot
- ☐ Skateboard
- ☐ Snake
- ☐ Star
- ☐ Sunglasses
- ☐ Tire
- ☐ Tree

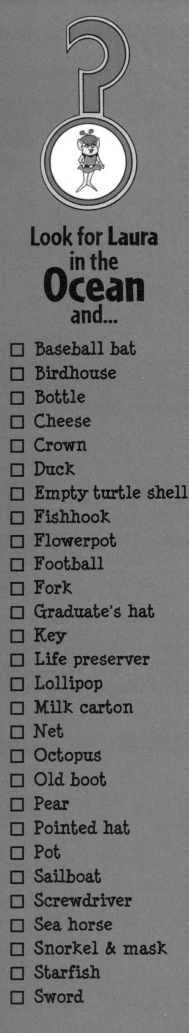

Look for Laura in the Ocean and...

- ☐ Baseball bat
- ☐ Birdhouse
- ☐ Bottle
- ☐ Cheese
- ☐ Crown
- ☐ Duck
- ☐ Empty turtle shell
- ☐ Fishhook
- ☐ Flowerpot
- ☐ Football
- ☐ Fork
- ☐ Graduate's hat
- ☐ Key
- ☐ Life preserver
- ☐ Lollipop
- ☐ Milk carton
- ☐ Net
- ☐ Octopus
- ☐ Old boot
- ☐ Pear
- ☐ Pointed hat
- ☐ Pot
- ☐ Sailboat
- ☐ Screwdriver
- ☐ Sea horse
- ☐ Snorkel & mask
- ☐ Starfish
- ☐ Sword

Look for **Laura** at the
Watering Hole
and...

- ☐ Baby bird
- ☐ Birdcage
- ☐ Briefcase
- ☐ Clothespins (2)
- ☐ Coconuts (4)
- ☐ Donkey
- ☐ Duck
- ☐ Feather
- ☐ Fish (3)
- ☐ Giraffe
- ☐ Headband
- ☐ Heart
- ☐ Hippo
- ☐ Leopard
- ☐ Lions (2)
- ☐ Log
- ☐ Lollipop
- ☐ Octopus
- ☐ Ping-pong paddle
- ☐ Radio
- ☐ Rhinoceros
- ☐ Robot
- ☐ Snake
- ☐ Turtle
- ☐ TV set
- ☐ Worm

Look for **Laura** on a **Ski Slope** in the **Alps** and...

- ☐ Balloon
- ☐ Barrels (2)
- ☐ Car
- ☐ Duck
- ☐ Earmuffs (3 pairs)
- ☐ Easel
- ☐ Elephant
- ☐ Frankenstein's monster
- ☐ Glove
- ☐ Headbands (2)
- ☐ Lamppost
- ☐ Lost boots (2)
- ☐ Lost ski
- ☐ Red bows (3)
- ☐ Scarves (7)
- ☐ Scuba diver
- ☐ Shovel
- ☐ "Soft Snow"
- ☐ Sunbather
- ☐ Telephone
- ☐ Telescope
- ☐ Tent
- ☐ Thrown snowball
- ☐ Train
- ☐ Tree

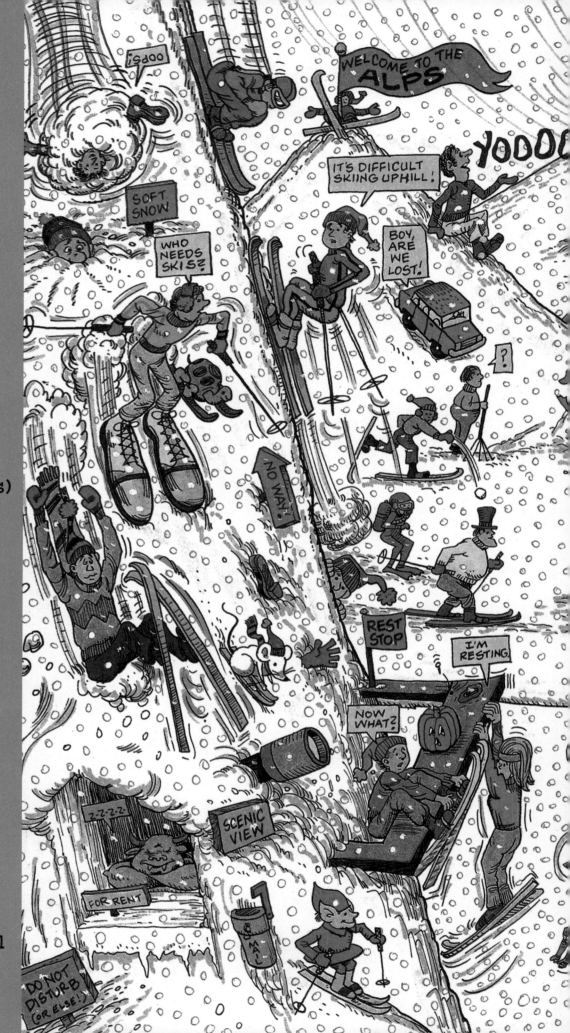

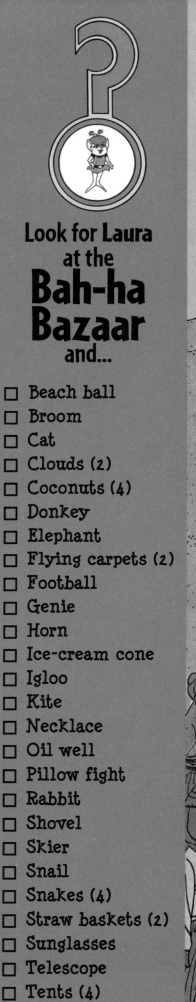

Look for **Laura** at the **Bah-ha Bazaar** and...

- ☐ Beach ball
- ☐ Broom
- ☐ Cat
- ☐ Clouds (2)
- ☐ Coconuts (4)
- ☐ Donkey
- ☐ Elephant
- ☐ Flying carpets (2)
- ☐ Football
- ☐ Genie
- ☐ Horn
- ☐ Ice-cream cone
- ☐ Igloo
- ☐ Kite
- ☐ Necklace
- ☐ Oil well
- ☐ Pillow fight
- ☐ Rabbit
- ☐ Shovel
- ☐ Skier
- ☐ Snail
- ☐ Snakes (4)
- ☐ Straw baskets (2)
- ☐ Sunglasses
- ☐ Telescope
- ☐ Tents (4)

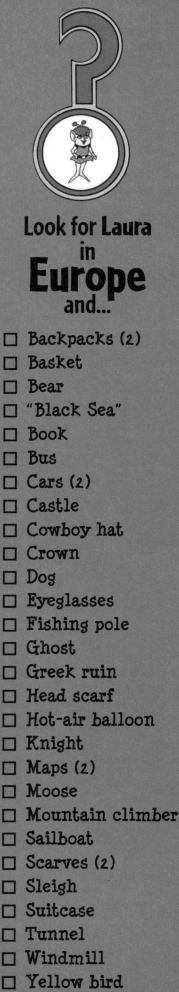

Look for Laura in Europe and...

- ☐ Backpacks (2)
- ☐ Basket
- ☐ Bear
- ☐ "Black Sea"
- ☐ Book
- ☐ Bus
- ☐ Cars (2)
- ☐ Castle
- ☐ Cowboy hat
- ☐ Crown
- ☐ Dog
- ☐ Eyeglasses
- ☐ Fishing pole
- ☐ Ghost
- ☐ Greek ruin
- ☐ Head scarf
- ☐ Hot-air balloon
- ☐ Knight
- ☐ Maps (2)
- ☐ Moose
- ☐ Mountain climber
- ☐ Sailboat
- ☐ Scarves (2)
- ☐ Sleigh
- ☐ Suitcase
- ☐ Tunnel
- ☐ Windmill
- ☐ Yellow bird

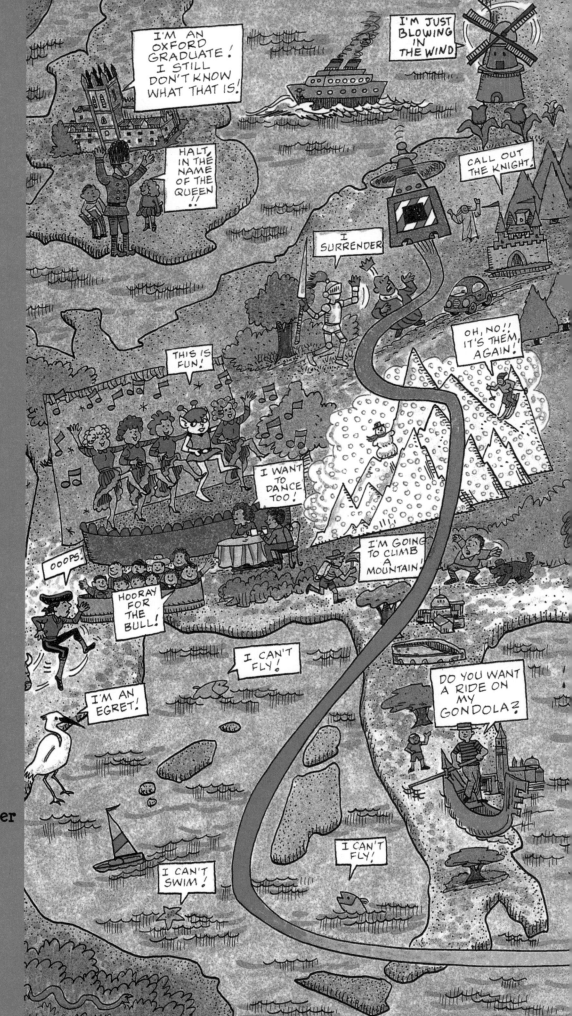

Look for Laura at Summer Camp and...

Look for **Laura** at the **Circus** and...

- [ ] Bandannas (2)
- [ ] Bicycle
- [ ] Bird
- [ ] Broom
- [ ] Car
- [ ] Cat
- [ ] Crown
- [ ] Drum
- [ ] Earmuff
- [ ] Flowerpot
- [ ] Flying shoe
- [ ] Football helmet
- [ ] Giraffe
- [ ] Lamp
- [ ] Mustaches (4)
- [ ] Padlock
- [ ] Paper bag
- [ ] Periscope
- [ ] Pointed hats (3)
- [ ] Propellers (2)
- [ ] Rabbit
- [ ] Ring of fire
- [ ] Sailor
- [ ] Santa Claus
- [ ] Straw hat
- [ ] Unhappy face
- [ ] Unicorn
- [ ] Whip

Look for Laura in Washington DC and...

- [ ] Baby kangaroo
- [ ] Balloons (2)
- [ ] Baseball cap
- [ ] Basket
- [ ] Capitol Building
- [ ] Dog
- [ ] Duck
- [ ] FBI agent
- [ ] Gloves
- [ ] Headband
- [ ] Jefferson Memorial
- [ ] Kite
- [ ] Mailbox
- [ ] Manhole
- [ ] Mouse
- [ ] Neckties (2)
- [ ] Paintbrush
- [ ] Pillow
- [ ] Ponytails (3)
- [ ] Red beret
- [ ] Sailor hat
- [ ] Spirit of St. Louis
- [ ] Sunglasses
- [ ] Tool box
- [ ] Tri-cornered hat
- [ ] Turtle
- [ ] Upside-down sign
- [ ] Wagon
- [ ] Yellow hat

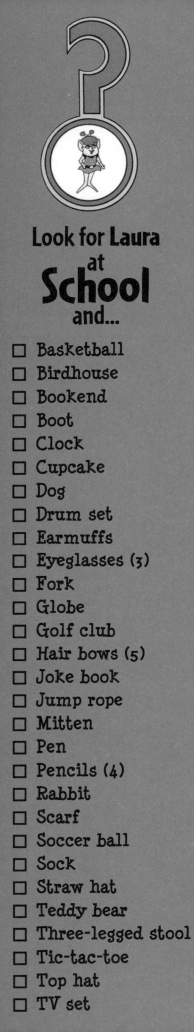

Look for **Laura** at **School** and...

- ☐ Basketball
- ☐ Birdhouse
- ☐ Bookend
- ☐ Boot
- ☐ Clock
- ☐ Cupcake
- ☐ Dog
- ☐ Drum set
- ☐ Earmuffs
- ☐ Eyeglasses (3)
- ☐ Fork
- ☐ Globe
- ☐ Golf club
- ☐ Hair bows (5)
- ☐ Joke book
- ☐ Jump rope
- ☐ Mitten
- ☐ Pen
- ☐ Pencils (4)
- ☐ Rabbit
- ☐ Scarf
- ☐ Soccer ball
- ☐ Sock
- ☐ Straw hat
- ☐ Teddy bear
- ☐ Three-legged stool
- ☐ Tic-tac-toe
- ☐ Top hat
- ☐ TV set

Look for **Laura** at the **Welcome Home Party** and...

- ☐ Balloons (2)
- ☐ Baseball
- ☐ Boot
- ☐ Bouquet of flowers
- ☐ Bowling ball
- ☐ Broom
- ☐ Dog
- ☐ Donut
- ☐ Fish
- ☐ Flowerpot
- ☐ Half-moons (2)
- ☐ Hearts (2)
- ☐ Ice-cream cone
- ☐ Manhole
- ☐ Nose
- ☐ Old tire
- ☐ Paddle
- ☐ Pail
- ☐ Pocket watch
- ☐ Scissors
- ☐ Screwdriver
- ☐ Stars (8)
- ☐ Straw
- ☐ Sunglasses
- ☐ Swiss cheese
- ☐ Top hat
- ☐ Turtle
- ☐ Yo-yo

DETECT DONALD

FIND FRANKIE

SEARCH FOR SUSIE

LOOK FOR LAURA

Search For Susie

Search for Susie in the Big Fun Park and...

- [ ] Baby dinosaurs (2)
- [ ] Bench
- [ ] Billy goat
- [ ] Blue jay
- [ ] Boot
- [ ] Cactus
- [ ] Cat
- [ ] Coffeepot
- [ ] Dollar sign
- [ ] Elephants (3)
- [ ] Fire hydrant
- [ ] Giraffes (2)
- [ ] Hamburgers (3)
- [ ] Kite
- [ ] Mice (2)
- [ ] Monkey
- [ ] Necklace
- [ ] Owl
- [ ] Pelican
- [ ] Penguin
- [ ] Periscopes (2)
- [ ] Pigs (4)
- [ ] Sailboat
- [ ] Sailor hat
- [ ] Scarecrow
- [ ] Stars (6)
- [ ] Wagon
- [ ] Susie's mom
- [ ] Telescope
- [ ] Unicorn
- [ ] Warthog
- [ ] Wolf

Search for Susie at the **Water Ride** and...

- ☐ Apple
- ☐ Beach ball
- ☐ Bib
- ☐ Bull
- ☐ Candles (2)
- ☐ Cats (2)
- ☐ Earring
- ☐ Elephants (2)
- ☐ Fishing pole
- ☐ Gorilla
- ☐ Hearts (2)
- ☐ Hot dog
- ☐ Kangaroo
- ☐ Paper bag
- ☐ Parrot
- ☐ Pencil
- ☐ Periscope
- ☐ Picnic basket
- ☐ Pitcher
- ☐ Puddles (4)
- ☐ Rabbits (2)
- ☐ Scuba diver
- ☐ Sheep
- ☐ Snakes (2)
- ☐ Sunglasses (2)
- ☐ Tents (3)
- ☐ Tire
- ☐ Turtle
- ☐ Wooden leg

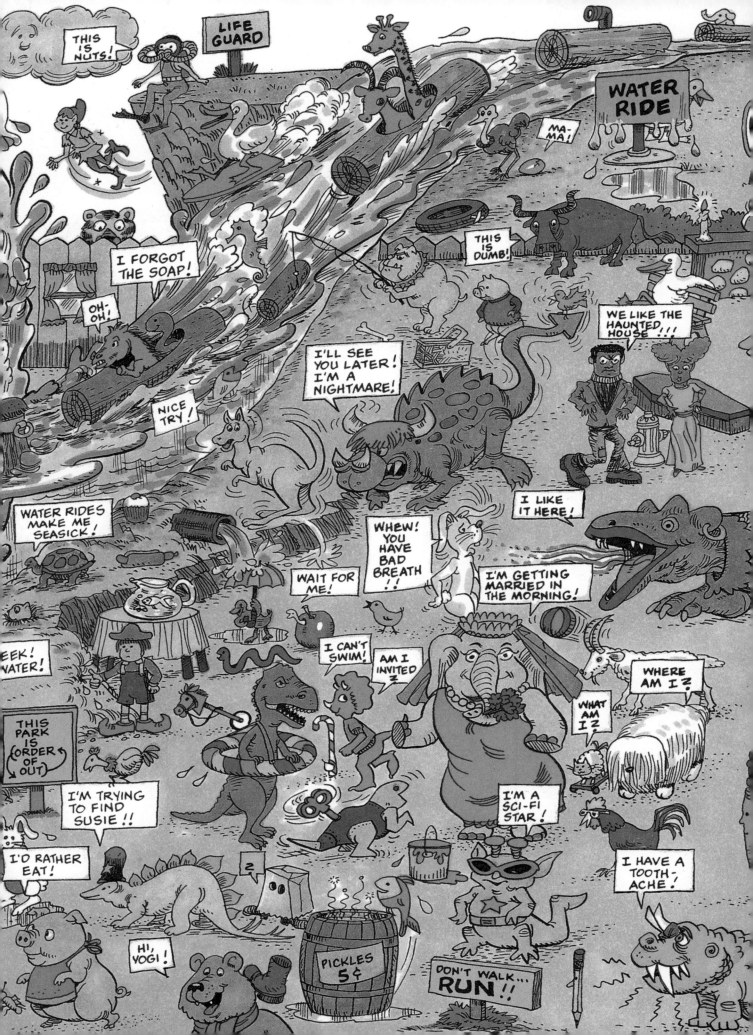

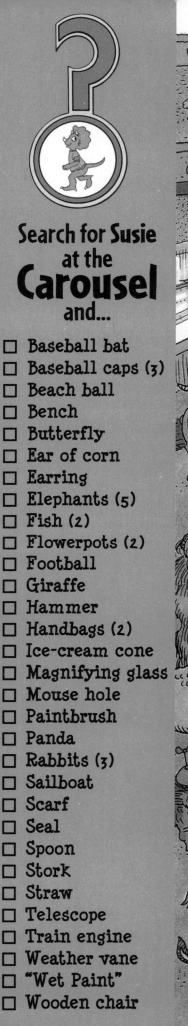

Search for Susie at the Carousel and...

- [ ] Baseball bat
- [ ] Baseball caps (3)
- [ ] Beach ball
- [ ] Bench
- [ ] Butterfly
- [ ] Ear of corn
- [ ] Earring
- [ ] Elephants (5)
- [ ] Fish (2)
- [ ] Flowerpots (2)
- [ ] Football
- [ ] Giraffe
- [ ] Hammer
- [ ] Handbags (2)
- [ ] Ice-cream cone
- [ ] Magnifying glass
- [ ] Mouse hole
- [ ] Paintbrush
- [ ] Panda
- [ ] Rabbits (3)
- [ ] Sailboat
- [ ] Scarf
- [ ] Seal
- [ ] Spoon
- [ ] Stork
- [ ] Straw
- [ ] Telescope
- [ ] Train engine
- [ ] Weather vane
- [ ] "Wet Paint"
- [ ] Wooden chair

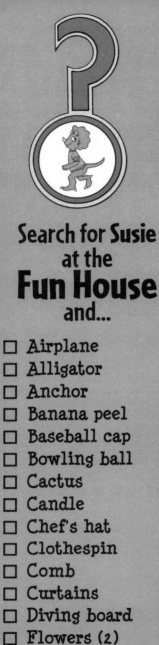

Search for **Susie** at the **Fun House** and...

- ☐ Airplane
- ☐ Alligator
- ☐ Anchor
- ☐ Banana peel
- ☐ Baseball cap
- ☐ Bowling ball
- ☐ Cactus
- ☐ Candle
- ☐ Chef's hat
- ☐ Clothespin
- ☐ Comb
- ☐ Curtains
- ☐ Diving board
- ☐ Flowers (2)
- ☐ Football
- ☐ Giraffes (2)
- ☐ Lamp
- ☐ Lollipop
- ☐ Lost boots (2)
- ☐ Masks (2)
- ☐ Mice (2)
- ☐ Pinocchio
- ☐ Pot
- ☐ Rabbits (3)
- ☐ Sailor hat
- ☐ Television
- ☐ Turtles (2)
- ☐ Vase
- ☐ Wall clocks (2)
- ☐ Wristwatch

Search for **Susie** at the **Ferris Wheel** and...

- ☐ Alarm clock
- ☐ Barrel
- ☐ Broken eggs
- ☐ Coffeepot
- ☐ Dog
- ☐ Ducks (3)
- ☐ Elephant
- ☐ Football
- ☐ Giraffe
- ☐ Gorilla
- ☐ Guitar
- ☐ Happy face
- ☐ Helicopter
- ☐ Jack-o'-lantern
- ☐ Jeep
- ☐ Ladders (2)
- ☐ Lions (2)
- ☐ Lost sneaker
- ☐ Mice (2)
- ☐ Neckties (4)
- ☐ Owl
- ☐ Paintbrushes (2)
- ☐ Popcorn
- ☐ Quicksand
- ☐ Shovel
- ☐ Snake
- ☐ Telephone
- ☐ Sock
- ☐ Statue
- ☐ Sunbather
- ☐ Sunglasses
- ☐ Trapdoor
- ☐ Volcano

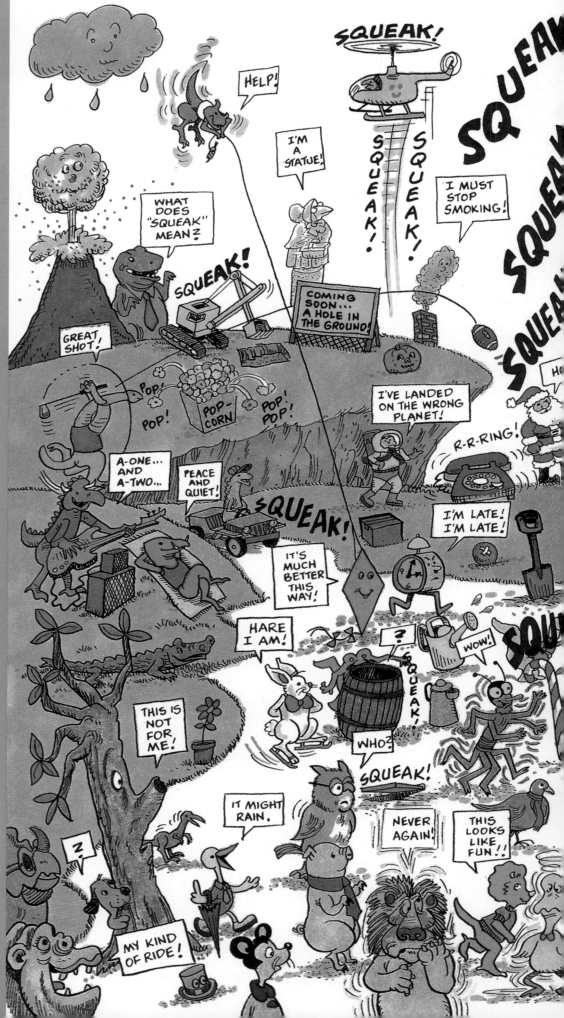

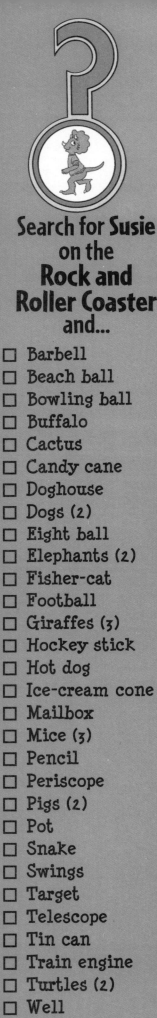

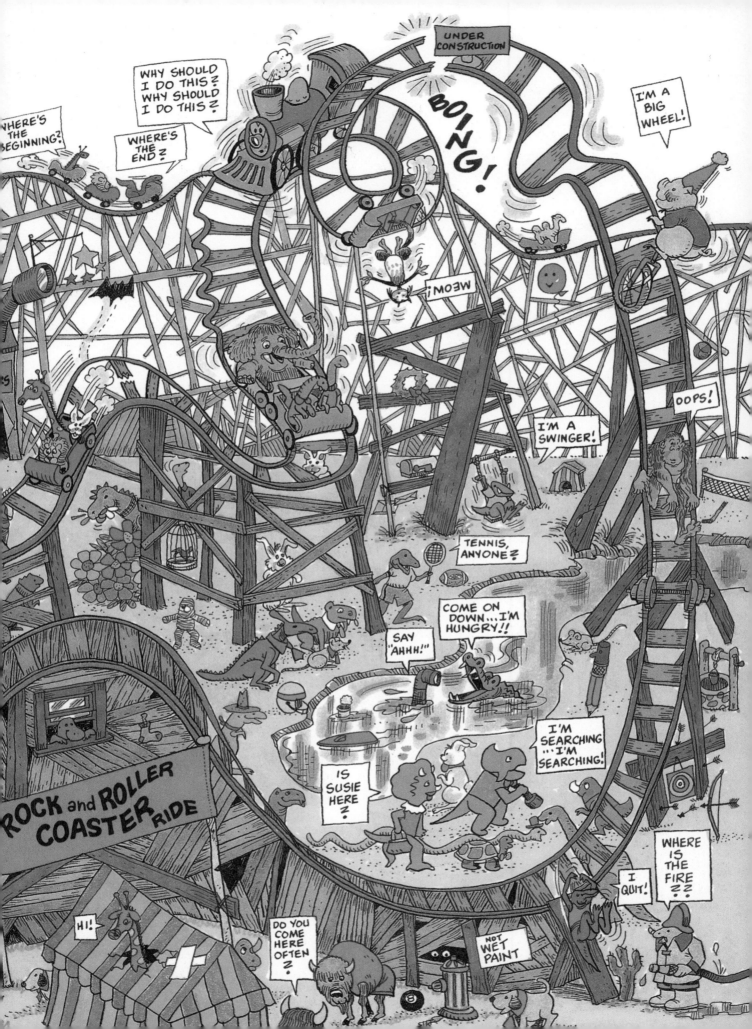

Search for Susie in the **Game Room** and...

- [ ] Banana
- [ ] Blindfold
- [ ] Bucket
- [ ] Cat
- [ ] Catcher's mitt
- [ ] Donkeys (2)
- [ ] "Don't Be Quiet"
- [ ] Dustpan
- [ ] Fake nose
- [ ] Flying reptile
- [ ] Football
- [ ] Graduate's hat
- [ ] Green bug
- [ ] Guitar
- [ ] Hairbrush
- [ ] Juggler
- [ ] Kangaroo
- [ ] Mouse house
- [ ] Picture frame
- [ ] Pie
- [ ] Rabbits (3)
- [ ] Ring toss
- [ ] Roller skate
- [ ] Sailboat
- [ ] Scarf
- [ ] Snake
- [ ] Toolbox
- [ ] Umbrella
- [ ] Watering can
- [ ] Watermelon slice
- [ ] Worm

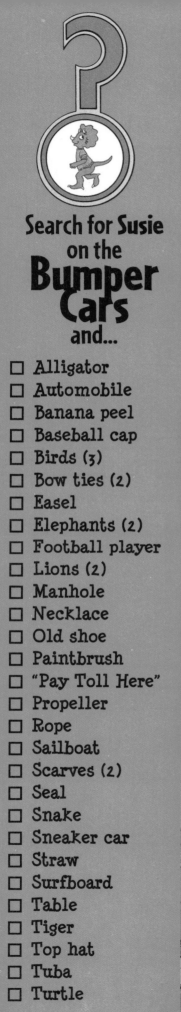

Search for Susie on the Bumper Cars and...

- ☐ Alligator
- ☐ Automobile
- ☐ Banana peel
- ☐ Baseball cap
- ☐ Birds (3)
- ☐ Bow ties (2)
- ☐ Easel
- ☐ Elephants (2)
- ☐ Football player
- ☐ Lions (2)
- ☐ Manhole
- ☐ Necklace
- ☐ Old shoe
- ☐ Paintbrush
- ☐ "Pay Toll Here"
- ☐ Propeller
- ☐ Rope
- ☐ Sailboat
- ☐ Scarves (2)
- ☐ Seal
- ☐ Snake
- ☐ Sneaker car
- ☐ Straw
- ☐ Surfboard
- ☐ Table
- ☐ Tiger
- ☐ Top hat
- ☐ Tuba
- ☐ Turtle

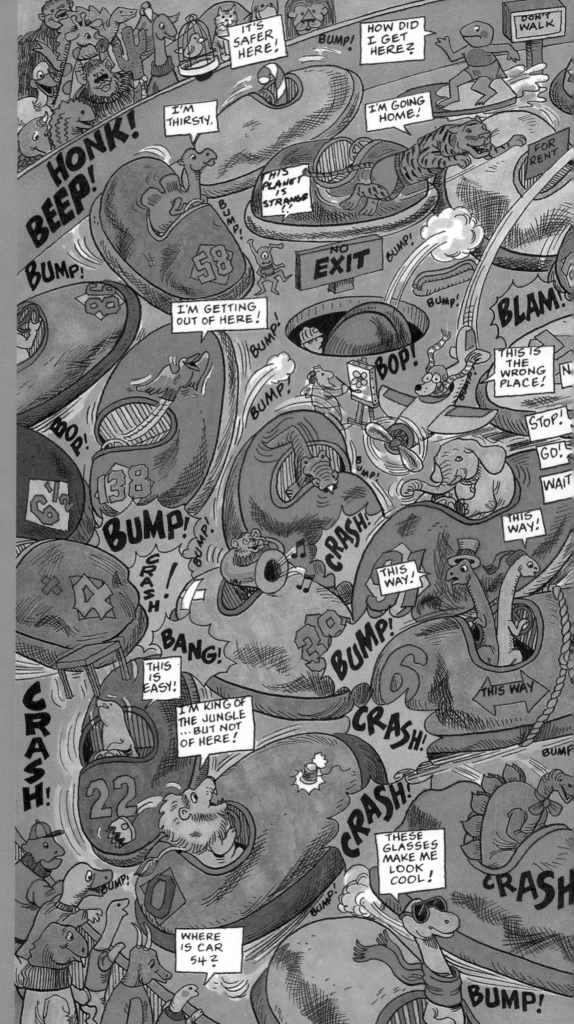

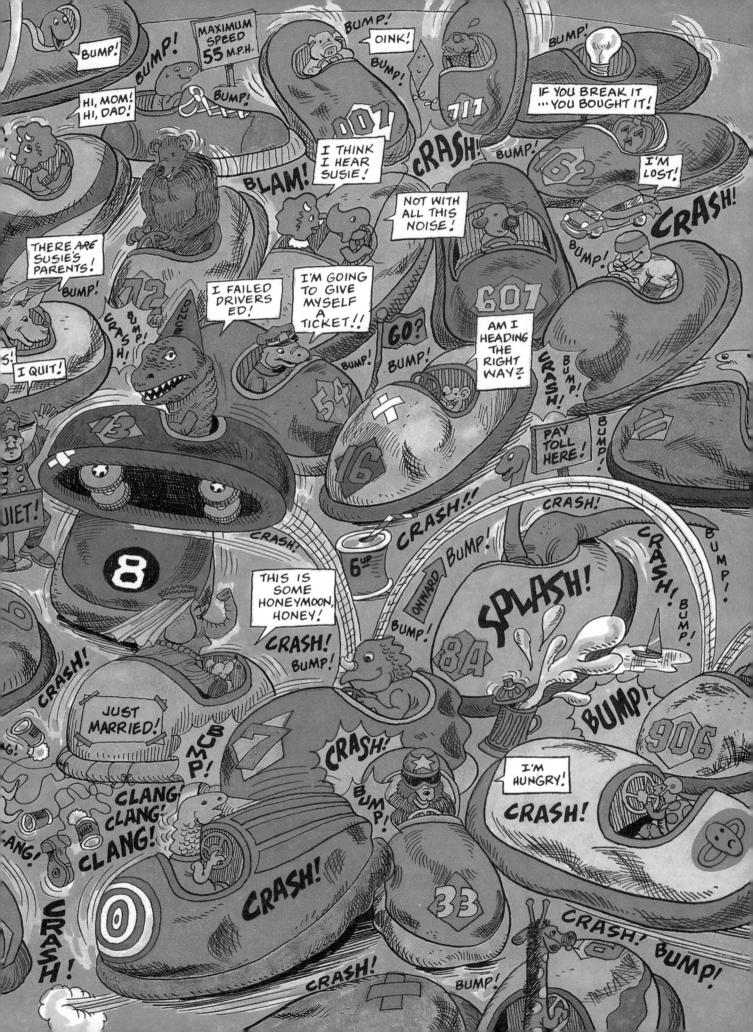

Search for Susie at the Ice Cream Shop and...

- ☐ Alien
- ☐ Banana peel
- ☐ Bowling ball
- ☐ Bubble gum
- ☐ Cactus
- ☐ Camel
- ☐ Candy cane
- ☐ Can of paint
- ☐ Clown
- ☐ Cow
- ☐ Flowerpot
- ☐ Flying carpet
- ☐ Flying reptiles (2)
- ☐ Football helmet
- ☐ Mice (3)
- ☐ Nail
- ☐ Parrot
- ☐ Pig
- ☐ Pillow
- ☐ Pocket watch
- ☐ Propeller hat
- ☐ Rocking horse
- ☐ Sailor hat
- ☐ Shovel
- ☐ Snake
- ☐ Star
- ☐ Straw
- ☐ Three-legged stool
- ☐ Turtle

Search for Susie on the Giant Swings and...

- ☐ Arrow
- ☐ Bears (2)
- ☐ Birdcage
- ☐ Bowling ball
- ☐ Candle
- ☐ Cat
- ☐ Dart
- ☐ Dogs (3)
- ☐ Elephants (2)
- ☐ Fishhook
- ☐ Football helmet
- ☐ Hot dog
- ☐ Ice skate
- ☐ Lamps (2)
- ☐ Lollipop
- ☐ Lost sneaker
- ☐ Magic lamp
- ☐ Monkey
- ☐ Mouse
- ☐ Penguin
- ☐ Propeller hat
- ☐ Rocket
- ☐ Scissors
- ☐ Soccer ball
- ☐ Sock
- ☐ Superhero
- ☐ Yo-yo

SEARCH FOR SUSIE   LOOK FOR LAURA   DETECT DONALD   FIND FRANKIE

WHERE ARE THEY?

FIND FREDDIE: AROUND THE WORLD

LOOK FOR LISA: TIME TRAVELER

SEARCH FOR SYLVESTER

WHERE'S WENDY?

Travel the world to find Freddie.

Travel through time to look for Lisa.

Search high and low for Sylvester.

Find out where Wendy could possibly be!

FREDDIE

LISA

WENDY

SYLVESTER

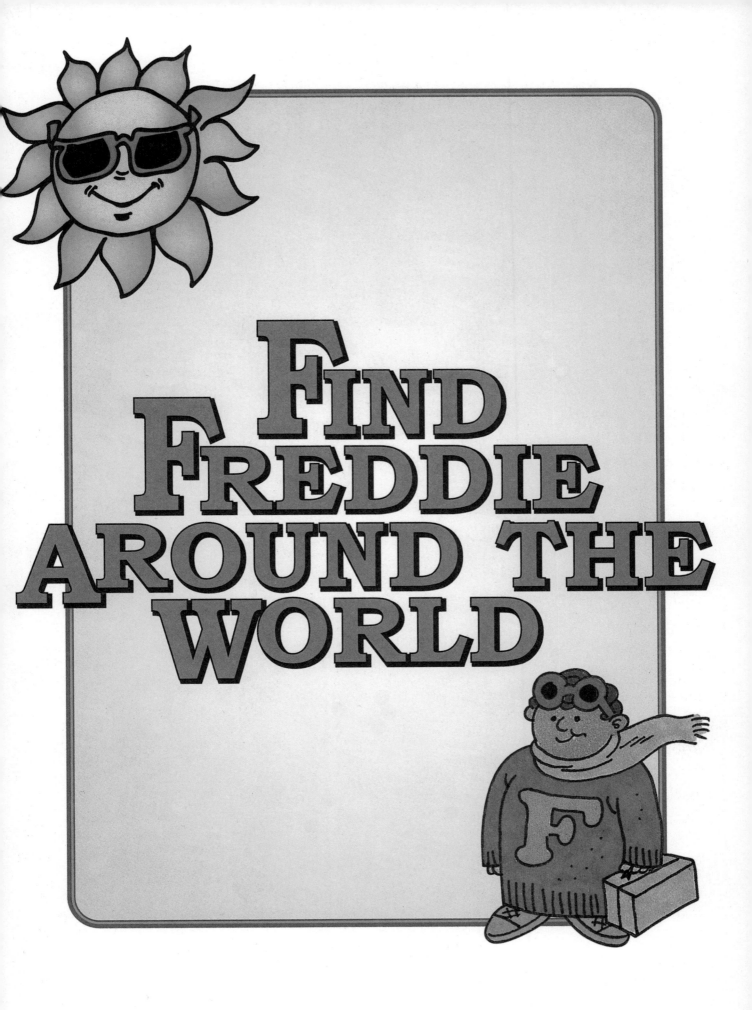

Find Freddie in the United States and...

- ☐ Alien
- ☐ Barbell
- ☐ Baseball player
- ☐ Beavers (2)
- ☐ Binoculars
- ☐ Carrot
- ☐ Cheese
- ☐ Cook
- ☐ Doctor
- ☐ Dog bone
- ☐ Dogs (2)
- ☐ Elephant
- ☐ Fire hydrant
- ☐ Football player
- ☐ Ice-cream cone
- ☐ Mice (3)
- ☐ Movie camera
- ☐ Octopus
- ☐ Palm trees (4)
- ☐ Rabbits (2)
- ☐ Skier
- ☐ Snake
- ☐ Snowman
- ☐ Stop sign
- ☐ Tent
- ☐ Trash can
- ☐ White House

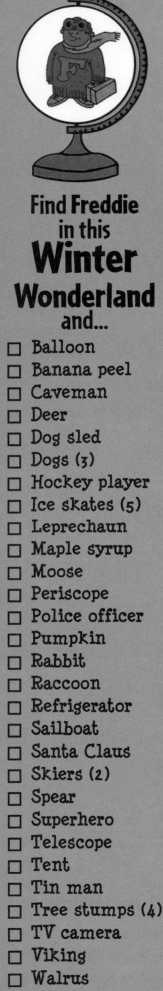

Find Freddie in this
Winter
Wonderland
and...

- [ ] Balloon
- [ ] Banana peel
- [ ] Caveman
- [ ] Deer
- [ ] Dog sled
- [ ] Dogs (3)
- [ ] Hockey player
- [ ] Ice skates (5)
- [ ] Leprechaun
- [ ] Maple syrup
- [ ] Moose
- [ ] Periscope
- [ ] Police officer
- [ ] Pumpkin
- [ ] Rabbit
- [ ] Raccoon
- [ ] Refrigerator
- [ ] Sailboat
- [ ] Santa Claus
- [ ] Skiers (2)
- [ ] Spear
- [ ] Superhero
- [ ] Telescope
- [ ] Tent
- [ ] Tin man
- [ ] Tree stumps (4)
- [ ] TV camera
- [ ] Viking
- [ ] Walrus

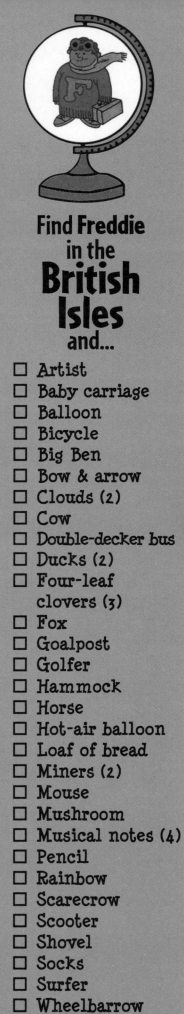

Find Freddie in the British Isles and...

- ☐ Artist
- ☐ Baby carriage
- ☐ Balloon
- ☐ Bicycle
- ☐ Big Ben
- ☐ Bow & arrow
- ☐ Clouds (2)
- ☐ Cow
- ☐ Double-decker bus
- ☐ Ducks (2)
- ☐ Four-leaf clovers (3)
- ☐ Fox
- ☐ Goalpost
- ☐ Golfer
- ☐ Hammock
- ☐ Horse
- ☐ Hot-air balloon
- ☐ Loaf of bread
- ☐ Miners (2)
- ☐ Mouse
- ☐ Mushroom
- ☐ Musical notes (4)
- ☐ Pencil
- ☐ Rainbow
- ☐ Scarecrow
- ☐ Scooter
- ☐ Shovel
- ☐ Socks
- ☐ Surfer
- ☐ Wheelbarrow

Find Freddie among these
Friendly
Foreigners
and...

- [ ] Anchor
- [ ] Antlers
- [ ] Baby
- [ ] Balloon
- [ ] Barn
- [ ] Bullfighter
- [ ] Camera
- [ ] Cheese
- [ ] Clothespins (4)
- [ ] Deer (2)
- [ ] Eagle scout
- [ ] Eiffel Tower
- [ ] Elephant
- [ ] Fisherman
- [ ] Greek ruins
- [ ] Kite
- [ ] Oil well
- [ ] Owl
- [ ] Panda
- [ ] Picnic basket
- [ ] Piggy bank
- [ ] Pyramid
- [ ] Rain slicker
- [ ] Telescope
- [ ] Umbrellas (2)
- [ ] Viking
- [ ] Windmill

Find Freddie
in this
Vast and Exotic Land
and...

- ☐ Alligator
- ☐ Bigfoot
- ☐ Black bear
- ☐ Bone
- ☐ Camels (2)
- ☐ Duck
- ☐ Elephant
- ☐ Gas pump
- ☐ Lion
- ☐ Magic carpet
- ☐ Mermaid
- ☐ Mongoose
- ☐ Monkey
- ☐ Mount Everest
- ☐ Mount Fuji
- ☐ Musical notes (11)
- ☐ Penguin
- ☐ Rhinoceros
- ☐ Sailboats (2)
- ☐ Sheep (2)
- ☐ Snowmen (2)
- ☐ Soccer ball
- ☐ Star
- ☐ Suez Canal
- ☐ Tea bag
- ☐ Umbrella
- ☐ Whale

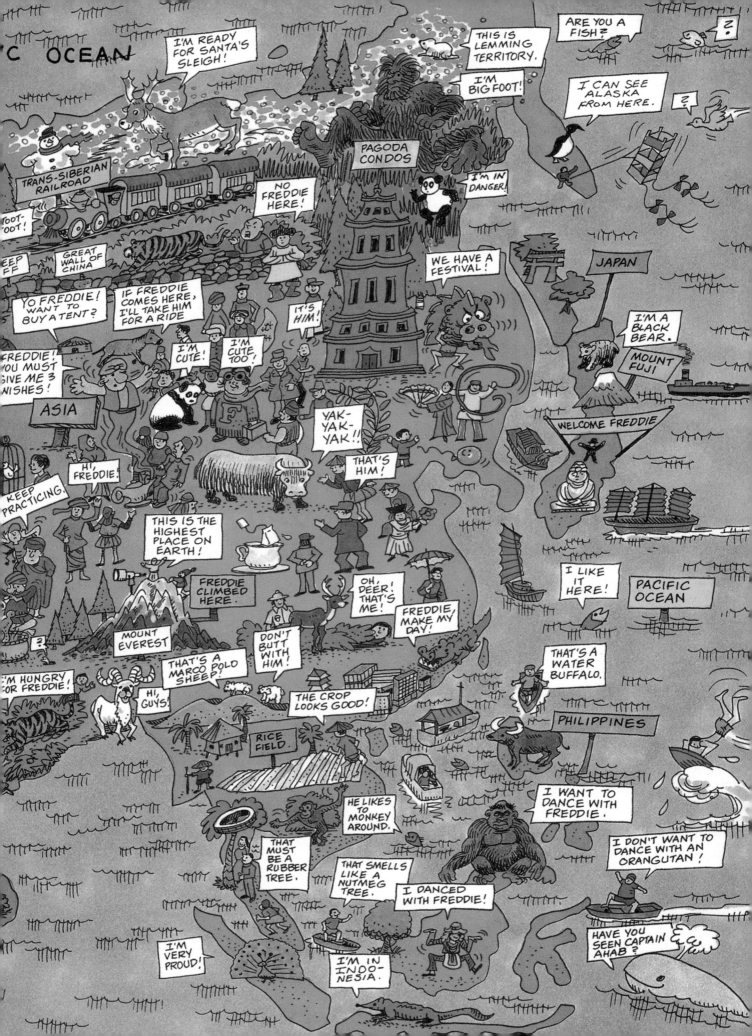

Find Freddie
in this
African
Adventure-Land
and...

- [ ] Alligator
- [ ] Ant
- [ ] Banana
- [ ] Bone
- [ ] Cat
- [ ] Crown
- [ ] Diamonds
- [ ] Donkey
- [ ] Egg
- [ ] Fishing nets (2)
- [ ] Fishing pole
- [ ] Flamingo
- [ ] Message in a bottle
- [ ] Moon
- [ ] Mug
- [ ] Mushroom
- [ ] Palm trees (3)
- [ ] Pyramid
- [ ] Rowboats (4)
- [ ] Santa Claus
- [ ] Seal
- [ ] Sunglasses (4)
- [ ] Surfboard
- [ ] Telescope
- [ ] Turtle
- [ ] Zebra

Find Freddie in the
Land
Down Under
and...

- [ ] Apples (7)
- [ ] Barbecue
- [ ] Boot
- [ ] Cloud
- [ ] Cow
- [ ] Crocodile
- [ ] Doctor
- [ ] Eggs (4)
- [ ] Emu
- [ ] Fishing poles (2)
- [ ] Ghost
- [ ] Guitar
- [ ] Lifeguard
- [ ] Message in a bottle
- [ ] Octopus
- [ ] Penguin
- [ ] Platypus
- [ ] Sailboats (2)
- [ ] Shark fins (5)
- [ ] Skiers (2)
- [ ] Snake
- [ ] Snowman
- [ ] Surfboards (9)
- [ ] Tasmanian devil
- [ ] Tennis rackets (4)
- [ ] Tire

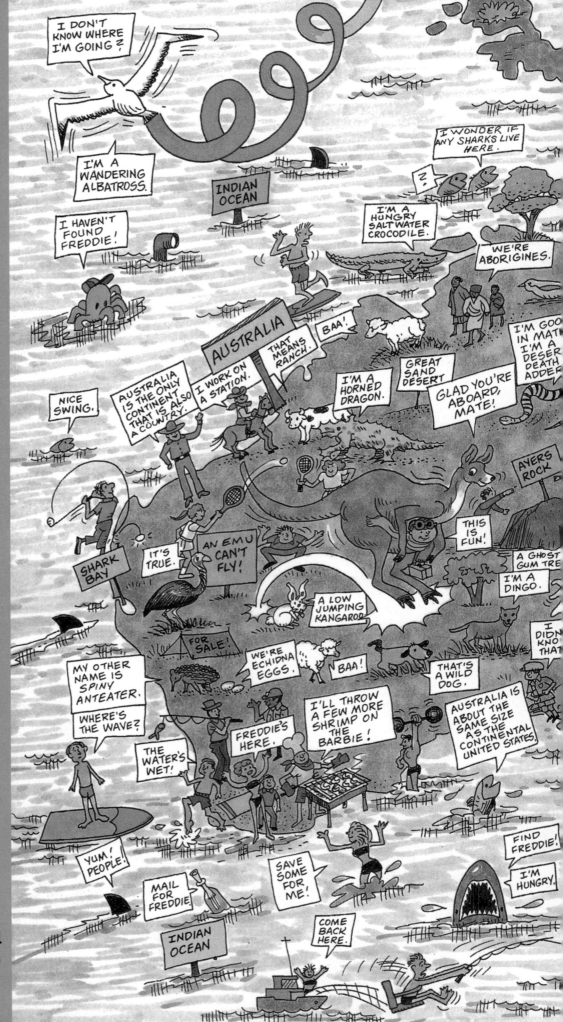

Find Freddie in this
Blistery Blizzard
and...

- ☐ Airplane
- ☐ Aliens (2)
- ☐ Baseball
- ☐ Box
- ☐ Campfire
- ☐ Circus tents (2)
- ☐ Easel
- ☐ Football
- ☐ Heart
- ☐ Helicopter
- ☐ Ice castle
- ☐ Ice skates (6)
- ☐ Jack-o'-lantern
- ☐ Kangaroo
- ☐ Kite
- ☐ Magic carpet
- ☐ Paintbrush
- ☐ Periscope
- ☐ Santa Claus
- ☐ Skis (4)
- ☐ Sleds (5)
- ☐ Spaceship
- ☐ Stars (2)
- ☐ Tennis racket
- ☐ Tin man
- ☐ Tombstone
- ☐ Top hats (2)

Find Freddie in
South America
and...

- ☐ Angel
- ☐ Ant
- ☐ Banana peel
- ☐ Beach ball
- ☐ Beehive
- ☐ Briefcase
- ☐ Candy bar
- ☐ Chinchilla
- ☐ Coconut
- ☐ Condor
- ☐ Dracula
- ☐ Flamingos (3)
- ☐ Flying bats (2)
- ☐ Iguana
- ☐ Jaguar
- ☐ Manatee
- ☐ Mouse
- ☐ Musical notes (3)
- ☐ Ostrich
- ☐ Penguin
- ☐ Pig
- ☐ Shark fins (2)
- ☐ Skull
- ☐ Spider
- ☐ Tires (2)
- ☐ Top hat
- ☐ Toucans (2)
- ☐ Tuba
- ☐ Waterfall

Find Freddie in Central America and...

- ☐ Banana tree
- ☐ Birdbath
- ☐ Bones (2)
- ☐ Broom
- ☐ Bucket
- ☐ Bull
- ☐ Cactus
- ☐ Camera
- ☐ Flying bats (2)
- ☐ Football
- ☐ Golfer
- ☐ Heart
- ☐ Hot-air balloon
- ☐ Kite
- ☐ Medal
- ☐ Periscope
- ☐ Pie
- ☐ Piggy bank
- ☐ Pizza
- ☐ Police officer
- ☐ Princess
- ☐ Rabbits (2)
- ☐ Sailboats (4)
- ☐ Snakes (2)
- ☐ Turtle
- ☐ Water skis
- ☐ Whale
- ☐ Wrench

Find Freddie on his
Last Stop
and...

- ☐ Alarm clock
- ☐ Apple
- ☐ Baseball player
- ☐ Beaver
- ☐ Cactus (2)
- ☐ Carrot
- ☐ Castle
- ☐ Cow
- ☐ Cowboys (2)
- ☐ Dogs (3)
- ☐ Hose
- ☐ Mermaid
- ☐ Moose
- ☐ Octopus
- ☐ Painted egg
- ☐ Paper airplane
- ☐ Parachute
- ☐ Periscope
- ☐ Refrigerator
- ☐ Sailboats (2)
- ☐ Sherlock Holmes
- ☐ Skunk
- ☐ Snowball
- ☐ Suit of armor
- ☐ Tents (2)
- ☐ Trash can
- ☐ Whales (2)
- ☐ Witch

Find Freddie and...

- ☐ Apple
- ☐ Baseball bat
- ☐ Birdcage
- ☐ Bucket
- ☐ Candle
- ☐ Cupcake
- ☐ Fire hydrant
- ☐ Flower
- ☐ Football helmet
- ☐ Frog
- ☐ Gift
- ☐ Hearts (2)
- ☐ Ice-cream cone
- ☐ Jump rope
- ☐ Medal
- ☐ Mitten
- ☐ Moon
- ☐ Mouse
- ☐ Pencil
- ☐ Pizza box
- ☐ Plate
- ☐ Rocking chair
- ☐ Turtle

LOOK FOR LISA: TIME TRAVELER

Look for Lisa in
Prehistoric Times
and...

- ☐ Baby carriage
- ☐ Candle
- ☐ Cherry
- ☐ Clothespin
- ☐ Dinosaur egg
- ☐ Faucet
- ☐ Four-leaf clover
- ☐ Hammer
- ☐ Hot chocolate
- ☐ Life preserver
- ☐ Message in a bottle
- ☐ Necklace
- ☐ Necktie
- ☐ "No U Turn"
- ☐ Palm trees (2)
- ☐ Periscope
- ☐ Piggy bank
- ☐ Pizza
- ☐ Ring
- ☐ Scarecrow
- ☐ Skateboard
- ☐ Stars (2)
- ☐ Swimming duck
- ☐ Tire
- ☐ Toothbrush
- ☐ Volcanoes (2)
- ☐ Wooden wheel

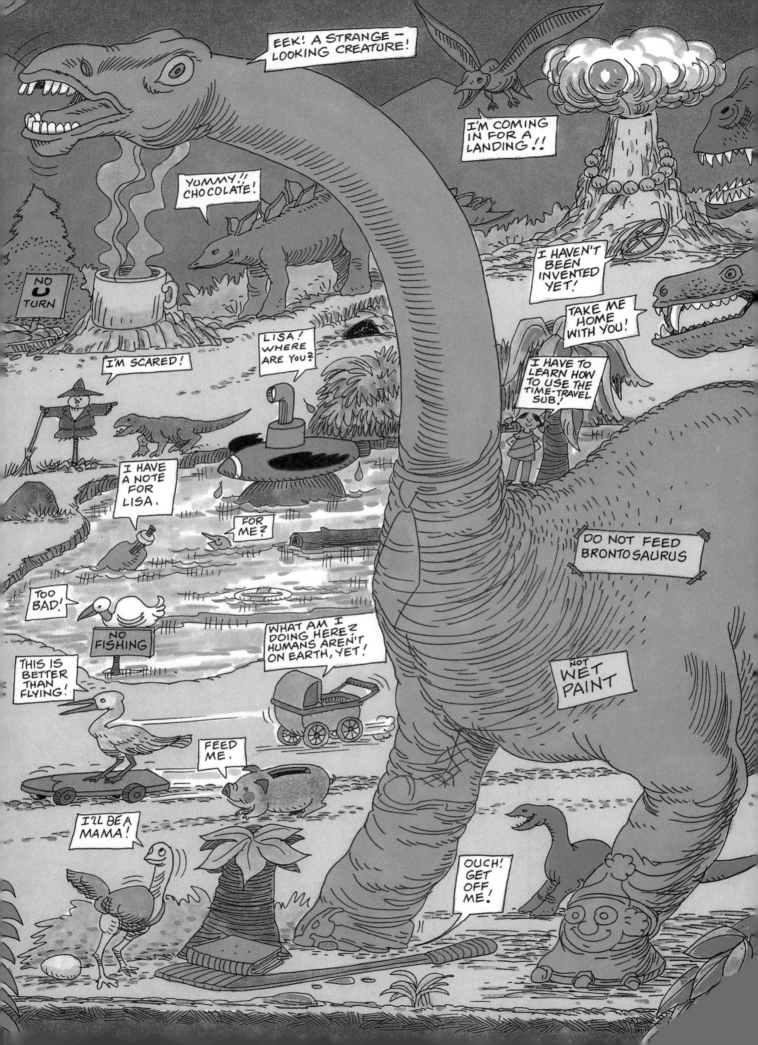

Look for Lisa in the
Creepy
Castle
and...

- ☐ Apples (2)
- ☐ Arrow
- ☐ Ball and chain
- ☐ Balloon
- ☐ Banana peel
- ☐ Baseball cap
- ☐ Birdcage
- ☐ Bones (6)
- ☐ Bowling pin
- ☐ Broom
- ☐ Calendar
- ☐ Carrot
- ☐ Crayon
- ☐ Door knocker
- ☐ Flying bats (3)
- ☐ Football
- ☐ Ghost
- ☐ Jar
- ☐ Lantern
- ☐ Mice (5)
- ☐ Nail
- ☐ Oil can
- ☐ Paintbrush
- ☐ Pencil
- ☐ Rose
- ☐ sors
- ☐ watch

Look for **Lisa** at this **Historic Happening** and...

- ☐ Antlers
- ☐ Axe
- ☐ Barrel
- ☐ Baseball bat
- ☐ Beach ball
- ☐ Bird
- ☐ Book
- ☐ Bow
- ☐ Bowl
- ☐ Candle
- ☐ Cat
- ☐ Dog
- ☐ Drums (2)
- ☐ Elephant
- ☐ Eyeglasses
- ☐ Flying bat
- ☐ Hair bows (5)
- ☐ Moon
- ☐ Mouse
- ☐ Pig
- ☐ Pot
- ☐ Puddles (4)
- ☐ Slice of pizza
- ☐ Snail
- ☐ Submarine
- ☐ ..r
- ☐ ..tump
- ☐ ..arrow

Look for **Lisa** as she **Rocks and Rolls** and...

Look for **Lisa** among these **Exciting Experiments** and...

- ☐ Apple cores (2)
- ☐ Arrow
- ☐ Axe
- ☐ Banana
- ☐ Bell
- ☐ Calendar
- ☐ Cannon
- ☐ Crayon
- ☐ Dart
- ☐ Fish
- ☐ Football
- ☐ Ghost
- ☐ Hamburger
- ☐ Hot-air balloon
- ☐ Jack-in-the-box
- ☐ Jack-o'-lantern
- ☐ Medals (2)
- ☐ Nut
- ☐ Piggy bank
- ☐ Puddle
- ☐ Sailboat
- ☐ Sardine can

Look for **Lisa** in these **Cavernous Craters** and...

- ☐ Axe
- ☐ Banana
- ☐ Bucket
- ☐ Car
- ☐ Clown
- ☐ Coffeepot
- ☐ Cup
- ☐ Duck
- ☐ Earth
- ☐ Envelope
- ☐ Fish
- ☐ Flashlight
- ☐ Heart
- ☐ Key
- ☐ Kite
- ☐ Ladder
- ☐ Mouse
- ☐ Penguin
- ☐ Pig
- ☐ Pumpkin
- ☐ Ring
- ☐ Saw
- ☐ Shovel
- ☐ Stamp
- ☐ Stars (4)
- ☐ Stool
- ☐ Toothbrush
- ☐ Turtle

Look for **Lisa** in the **Ocean** and...

- [ ] Baby
- [ ] Barrel
- [ ] Baseball bat
- [ ] Basketball
- [ ] Boot
- [ ] Bucket
- [ ] Captain's hat
- [ ] Elephant
- [ ] Fish (3)
- [ ] Guitar
- [ ] Harp
- [ ] Heart
- [ ] Homework
- [ ] Hot-air balloon
- [ ] Ice-cream cone
- [ ] Key
- [ ] Oars (5)
- [ ] Painting
- [ ] Palm tree
- [ ] Scuba diver
- [ ] Shark fins (2)
- [ ] Slice of watermelon
- [ ] Sock
- [ ] Surfer
- [ ] Television
- [ ] Tin can
- [ ] Tire
- [ ] Tree

Look for **Lisa** at this **Special Celebration** and...

- ☐ Axe
- ☐ Barrel
- ☐ Basketball
- ☐ Bear
- ☐ Boat
- ☐ Book
- ☐ Bowling ball
- ☐ Chef
- ☐ Duck
- ☐ Ears of corn (2)
- ☐ Feather
- ☐ Fish
- ☐ Handkerchief
- ☐ Magnifying glass
- ☐ Mouse
- ☐ Owl
- ☐ Paintbrush
- ☐ Pizza delivery
- ☐ Pumpkins (3)
- ☐ Smoke signals
- ☐ Spoon
- ☐ Telephone
- ☐ Tepees (2)
- ☐ Turkeys (2)
- ☐ Turtle
- ☐ Watering can
- ☐ Wedding cake
- ☐ Worm

Look for Lisa at Thomas Edison's Lab and...

- ☐ Bandannas (5)
- ☐ Birdcage
- ☐ Briefcase
- ☐ Cat
- ☐ Chairs (2)
- ☐ Clipboards (2)
- ☐ Club
- ☐ Cookies
- ☐ Cowboy hats (4)
- ☐ Curtains
- ☐ Eyeglasses
- ☐ Film projector
- ☐ Fish
- ☐ Hammer
- ☐ Pail
- ☐ Periscope
- ☐ Picture
- ☐ Plant
- ☐ Poodle
- ☐ Rain slicker
- ☐ Roller skates
- ☐ Sailboat
- ☐ Screwdriver
- ☐ Shadow
- ☐ Sheep
- ☐ Trash can
- ☐ Triangle
- ☐ Turtle

Look for Lisa among these Friendly Aliens and...

- [ ] Airplane
- [ ] Basketball hoop
- [ ] Bowling ball
- [ ] Briefcase
- [ ] Cactus
- [ ] Crayon
- [ ] Cup
- [ ] Desk lamp
- [ ] Donut
- [ ] Envelope
- [ ] Flower
- [ ] Hamburger
- [ ] Hose
- [ ] Hot dog
- [ ] Musical note
- [ ] "No Parking"
- [ ] Paintbrush
- [ ] Pencils (2)
- [ ] Pirates (2)
- [ ] Pyramid
- [ ] Straw
- [ ] Target
- [ ] Television
- [ ] Top hat
- [ ] Train
- [ ] Trash can
- [ ] Trees (3)
- [ ] Yo-yo

Look for **Lisa** at the **Magic Show** and...

- ☐ Apple
- ☐ Barbell
- ☐ Barrel
- ☐ Beard
- ☐ Box
- ☐ Burned-out light bulbs (2)
- ☐ Dragon
- ☐ Elephants (2)
- ☐ Football
- ☐ Graduation cap
- ☐ Headband
- ☐ Heart
- ☐ Jack-o'-lantern
- ☐ Key
- ☐ Knight
- ☐ Leaf
- ☐ Mouse
- ☐ Palm tree
- ☐ Puppy
- ☐ Purple hat
- ☐ Rabbit
- ☐ Sandbag
- ☐ Snake
- ☐ Top hat
- ☐ Trapdoors (2)
- ☐ Weightlifter
- ☐ Whale

Look for Lisa and...

- [ ] Baseball bat
- [ ] Bird
- [ ] Bottle
- [ ] Broom
- [ ] Cactus
- [ ] Can
- [ ] Cane
- [ ] Fire hydrant
- [ ] Fish
- [ ] Flowers (2)
- [ ] Hammers (2)
- [ ] Kite
- [ ] Moon
- [ ] Octopus
- [ ] Rabbit
- [ ] Saw
- [ ] Scarves (2)
- [ ] Snake
- [ ] Sun
- [ ] Tire
- [ ] Top hat
- [ ] Turtle
- [ ] Wreath

Search for Sylvester at this Mad Mall and...

- ☐ Astronaut
- ☐ Balloon
- ☐ Barber pole
- ☐ Bone
- ☐ Bride
- ☐ Briefcase
- ☐ Cat
- ☐ Cowboy hat
- ☐ Feathers (2)
- ☐ Fish (2)
- ☐ King
- ☐ Ladder
- ☐ Manhole
- ☐ Moon
- ☐ Mouse
- ☐ Musical note
- ☐ Parachute
- ☐ Pizza
- ☐ Robin Hood
- ☐ Sailboat
- ☐ Scarecrow
- ☐ Shopping bag
- ☐ Skier
- ☐ Stool
- ☐ Stuffed elephant
- ☐ Tin man
- ☐ Top hat
- ☐ Winter hats (2)

Search for Sylvester in this Fun-Filled Playground and...

- ☐ Arrows (3)
- ☐ Ballerina
- ☐ Banana peel
- ☐ Beach ball
- ☐ Birdcage
- ☐ Birdhouse
- ☐ Birds (4)
- ☐ Bowling pin
- ☐ Cactus
- ☐ Cannon
- ☐ Diploma
- ☐ Dracula
- ☐ Ducklings (4)
- ☐ Eight ball
- ☐ Fire hydrant
- ☐ Flying bat
- ☐ Hockey stick
- ☐ Lamp
- ☐ Newspapers (2)
- ☐ Paint bucket
- ☐ Police officer
- ☐ Propeller hat
- ☐ Rooster
- ☐ Saws (2)
- ☐ Shovel
- ☐ Superhero
- ☐ Turtle
- ☐ Wagon
- ☐ Wheels (2)
- ☐ Yellow hat

Search for Sylvester at Fast Food Heaven and...

- ☐ Alligator
- ☐ Bone
- ☐ Bowling ball
- ☐ Carrot
- ☐ Club
- ☐ Crowns (2)
- ☐ Dogs (2)
- ☐ Drum
- ☐ Elf
- ☐ Flying bat
- ☐ Football player
- ☐ Frog
- ☐ Ice-cream cone
- ☐ Jack-o'-lantern
- ☐ Jogger
- ☐ Kite
- ☐ Mouse
- ☐ Owl
- ☐ Pickle
- ☐ Popped balloon
- ☐ Rabbit
- ☐ Shopping bag
- ☐ Skier
- ☐ Snowman
- ☐ Tire
- ☐ Trees (2)
- ☐ Tugboat
- ☐ Turtle
- ☐ Witch
- ☐ Worm

Search for Sylvester at the Zany Zoo and...

- ☐ Baseball bat
- ☐ Baseball caps (4)
- ☐ Bow tie
- ☐ Camel
- ☐ Fish
- ☐ Football
- ☐ Girl with pigtails
- ☐ Kangaroo
- ☐ Little Red Riding Hood
- ☐ Neckties (3)
- ☐ Owl
- ☐ Parrot
- ☐ Pig
- ☐ Pine tree
- ☐ Rabbit
- ☐ Raccoon
- ☐ Scarf
- ☐ School bus
- ☐ Sea horse
- ☐ Seal
- ☐ Shovel
- ☐ Spoon
- ☐ Telescope
- ☐ Top hat
- ☐ Toy turtle
- ☐ Trash can
- ☐ Turtle
- ☐ Waiter

Search for **Sylvester** in this **Alphabetical School** and...

☐ A
☐ B
☐ C
☐ D
☐ E
☐ F
☐ G
☐ H
☐ I
☐ J
☐ K
☐ L
☐ M
☐ N
☐ O
☐ P
☐ Q
☐ R
☐ S
☐ T
☐ U
☐ V
☐ W
☐ X
☐ Y
☐ Z

Search for Sylvester at the Basketball Game and...

- ☐ Alligator
- ☐ Balloons (2)
- ☐ Banana peel
- ☐ Baseball
- ☐ Bowling ball
- ☐ Cannon
- ☐ Cherry
- ☐ Envelopes (2)
- ☐ Eyeglasses (2)
- ☐ Football helmet
- ☐ Ghost
- ☐ Headbands (2)
- ☐ Hot dog
- ☐ Jack-o'-lantern
- ☐ Kangaroo
- ☐ Kite
- ☐ Lost glove
- ☐ Pail
- ☐ Pencil
- ☐ Pizza box
- ☐ Police officer
- ☐ Pom poms (4)
- ☐ Rabbit
- ☐ Snake
- ☐ Stars (3)
- ☐ Tarzan
- ☐ Turtle

Search for Sylvester at this Spooky Mansion and...

- ☐ Arrows (2)
- ☐ Book
- ☐ Brush
- ☐ Bucket
- ☐ Candle
- ☐ Carrot
- ☐ Cauldron
- ☐ Curtains
- ☐ Flower
- ☐ Flying bat
- ☐ Football
- ☐ Ghost
- ☐ Hammer
- ☐ Lawn mower
- ☐ Letter
- ☐ Old tire
- ☐ Piano keys
- ☐ Shovel
- ☐ Skulls (2)
- ☐ Spiderweb
- ☐ Sword
- ☐ Tin can
- ☐ Trash can lid
- ☐ Vulture
- ☐ Wagon
- ☐ Watering can
- ☐ Witch

Search for
Sylvester
at
Detective
Donald's Digs
and...

- ☐ Broken pencils (3)
- ☐ Calendar
- ☐ Can
- ☐ Candles (3)
- ☐ Chalk
- ☐ Chalkboard
- ☐ Cheese
- ☐ Comb
- ☐ Diploma
- ☐ Fan
- ☐ Fishing pole
- ☐ Jacket
- ☐ Key
- ☐ Ladder
- ☐ Lamp
- ☐ Medal
- ☐ Nail
- ☐ Paint bucket
- ☐ Roller skate
- ☐ Screwdriver
- ☐ Shovel
- ☐ Skull
- ☐ Snake
- ☐ Stack of envelopes
- ☐ Sword
- ☐ Tack
- ☐ Top hat
- ☐ Trunk

Search for Sylvester at this Silly Circus and...

- ☐ Balloon with star
- ☐ Barrel
- ☐ Cactus
- ☐ Cake
- ☐ Camel
- ☐ Cannon
- ☐ Clothespins (3)
- ☐ Clowns (4)
- ☐ Crayon
- ☐ Firefighter
- ☐ Flowerpot
- ☐ Light bulb
- ☐ Mice (2)
- ☐ Necktie
- ☐ Party hat
- ☐ Pinocchio
- ☐ Pizza
- ☐ Police officer
- ☐ Skateboard
- ☐ Snowman
- ☐ Spoon
- ☐ Stars (5)
- ☐ Teacup
- ☐ Tin man
- ☐ Unicycle
- ☐ Witch
- ☐ Wizard hat
- ☐ Worm

Search for Sylvester as he Soars Through the Sky and...

- ☐ Ape
- ☐ Banana
- ☐ Baseball bat
- ☐ Bathtub
- ☐ Bird
- ☐ Bow
- ☐ Carrot
- ☐ Cupcake
- ☐ Fishermen (2)
- ☐ Flowers (4)
- ☐ Flying bat
- ☐ Football player
- ☐ Guitar
- ☐ Moon
- ☐ Pot
- ☐ Scarecrow
- ☐ Scarf
- ☐ Shovel
- ☐ Spaceship
- ☐ Stars (3)
- ☐ Sunglasses
- ☐ Target
- ☐ Teapot
- ☐ Tent
- ☐ TV antenna
- ☐ Watering can
- ☐ Witch

Search for
Sylvester
in
Bamboo Town
and...

- ☐ Balloons (2)
- ☐ Brooms (2)
- ☐ Drum
- ☐ Eyeglasses (2)
- ☐ Fire hydrants (2)
- ☐ Football
- ☐ Football player
- ☐ Ghost
- ☐ Gift
- ☐ Hard hats (2)
- ☐ Heart
- ☐ Horseshoe
- ☐ Ice-cream cones (2)
- ☐ Jump rope
- ☐ Kangaroo
- ☐ Knight
- ☐ Mask
- ☐ Medal
- ☐ Octopus
- ☐ Pencil
- ☐ Periscope
- ☐ Record
- ☐ Socks (3)
- ☐ Stool
- ☐ Straw
- ☐ Telescope
- ☐ Wizard
- ☐ Worm

Search for Sylvester and...

Apple
Bamboo shoot
Baseball
Bone
Candle
Cane

- ☐ Carrot
- ☐ Cupcake
- ☐ Drum
- ☐ Fire hydrant
- ☐ Flag
- ☐ Flowers (10)

- ☐ Football
- ☐ Horn
- ☐ Kite
- ☐ Leaf
- ☐ Lock
- ☐ Moon

- ☐ Paintbrush
- ☐ Screwdriver
- ☐ Spoon
- ☐ Top hat
- ☐ Turtle

WHERE'S WENDY?

Find Wendy at
Witchville
High School
and...

- [ ] Apple
- [ ] Axe
- [ ] Baseball bat
- [ ] Bear
- [ ] Bell
- [ ] Blimp
- [ ] Bowling ball
- [ ] Cauldrons (2)
- [ ] Dog
- [ ] Flying bats (2)
- [ ] Football
- [ ] Green hand
- [ ] Headless man
- [ ] Mask
- [ ] Mushrooms (3)
- [ ] One-eyed monsters (2)
- [ ] Pencil
- [ ] Piece of paper
- [ ] Scarecrow
- [ ] Shovel
- [ ] Skateboard
- [ ] Tire
- [ ] Tombstones (3)
- [ ] Turtle
- [ ] TV antenna
- [ ] Unicorn
- [ ] Walking tree
- [ ] Worm

Find Wendy in the
Classroom
and...

- [ ] Baseball bat
- [ ] Bell
- [ ] Bones (2)
- [ ] Books (6)
- [ ] Broken egg
- [ ] Button
- [ ] Clock
- [ ] Eight ball
- [ ] Eyeglasses (2)
- [ ] Flying bats (2)
- [ ] Football
- [ ] Hourglass
- [ ] Ice-cream cone
- [ ] Jack-o'-lantern
- [ ] Key
- [ ] Magic wand
- [ ] Marshmallow
- [ ] Needle
- [ ] Octopus
- [ ] Piece of chalk
- [ ] Pizza
- [ ] Rabbit
- [ ] Saw
- [ ] Scissors
- [ ] Skeleton
- [ ] Skunk
- [ ] Stool
- [ ] Straw
- [ ] Umbrella

Find Wendy on the **Witches' Class Trip** and...

- ☐ Apple
- ☐ Basket
- ☐ Basketball
- ☐ Bird
- ☐ Cactus
- ☐ Chair
- ☐ Chicken
- ☐ Crayon
- ☐ Crocodile
- ☐ Dogs (2)
- ☐ Faucet
- ☐ Flowers (2)
- ☐ Flying bat
- ☐ Football
- ☐ Hammer
- ☐ Hearts (2)
- ☐ Hockey stick
- ☐ Ice-cream cone
- ☐ Mitten
- ☐ Paintbrush
- ☐ Paint bucket
- ☐ Painted egg
- ☐ Periscope
- ☐ Pizza slice
- ☐ Squirrel
- ☐ Sunglasses (2)
- ☐ Top hat
- ☐ Watermelon slice

Find Wendy in the
Lunchroom
and...

- ☐ Apple
- ☐ Bird
- ☐ Broken nose
- ☐ Cactus
- ☐ Candle
- ☐ Cat
- ☐ Chick
- ☐ Cookbook
- ☐ Crystal ball
- ☐ Cymbals (2)
- ☐ Drum
- ☐ Flower
- ☐ Football
- ☐ Frying pans (3)
- ☐ Graduate
- ☐ Lighthouse
- ☐ Musical notes (3)
- ☐ Paper airplane
- ☐ Plate of cookies
- ☐ Santa Claus
- ☐ Skull
- ☐ Snakes (2)
- ☐ Straw
- ☐ Teapot
- ☐ Trash can
- ☐ Turtle
- ☐ Volcano
- ☐ Yellow hand
- ☐ Yellow sock

Look for **Wendy** during **Final Exams** and...

- ☐ Ball of yarn
- ☐ Balloon
- ☐ Baseball cap
- ☐ Broken mirror
- ☐ Broken pot
- ☐ Brooms (2)
- ☐ Cheese
- ☐ Chicken
- ☐ Clipboards (4)
- ☐ Cloud
- ☐ Coonskin cap
- ☐ Doctor
- ☐ Duck
- ☐ Elephant
- ☐ Flying bats (3)
- ☐ Football
- ☐ Heart
- ☐ Jack-o'-lantern
- ☐ Lost mitten
- ☐ Magic lamp
- ☐ Mouse
- ☐ Pencil
- ☐ Pogo stick
- ☐ Saw
- ☐ Skulls (2)
- ☐ Stool
- ☐ Tombstone
- ☐ Trunk
- ☐ Worm

Hunt for Wendy at
Graduation
and...

- ☐ Barbell
- ☐ Bones (2)
- ☐ Broken mirror
- ☐ Brooms (3)
- ☐ Can
- ☐ Candle
- ☐ Cracked egg
- ☐ Dog
- ☐ Drum
- ☐ Flying bats (2)
- ☐ Ghost
- ☐ Graduation cap
- ☐ Guitar
- ☐ Kite
- ☐ Marshmallow
- ☐ Moons (2)
- ☐ Musical note
- ☐ Panda
- ☐ Pumpkins (2)
- ☐ Robot
- ☐ Sled
- ☐ Target
- ☐ Tire
- ☐ Tombstones (13)
- ☐ Toolbox
- ☐ Turtle
- ☐ Umbrella
- ☐ Wizard
- ☐ Worm

Find Wendy in
Count Dracula's Living Room
and...

- ☐ Airplane
- ☐ Baseball bat
- ☐ Birdcage
- ☐ Book
- ☐ Brooms (3)
- ☐ Chair
- ☐ Chicken
- ☐ Cracked egg
- ☐ Crayon
- ☐ Dustpan
- ☐ Globe
- ☐ Mice (3)
- ☐ Mouse hole
- ☐ Mummy
- ☐ Owl
- ☐ Paintbrush
- ☐ Piano keys
- ☐ Pig
- ☐ Pitcher
- ☐ Spiderweb
- ☐ Teacup
- ☐ Teapot
- ☐ Telephone
- ☐ Top hat
- ☐ Umbrellas (3)
- ☐ Vacuum
- ☐ Worm
- ☐ Wreath

Search for **Wendy** in **Dr. Frankenstein's Laboratory** and...

- ☐ Ball of yarn
- ☐ Banana
- ☐ Baseball cap
- ☐ Bird
- ☐ Boot
- ☐ Bow
- ☐ Bucket
- ☐ Candles (2)
- ☐ Cheese
- ☐ Clock
- ☐ Eight ball
- ☐ Eyeglasses
- ☐ Flowers (2)
- ☐ Flying bat
- ☐ Fork
- ☐ Hammer
- ☐ Heart
- ☐ Lips
- ☐ Mask
- ☐ Mice (4)
- ☐ Needle & thread
- ☐ Pig
- ☐ Pizza
- ☐ Present
- ☐ Pumpkin
- ☐ Saw
- ☐ Spoon
- ☐ Stars (4)
- ☐ Stool
- ☐ Watermelon

Hunt for **Wendy** in the **Mummy's Tomb** and...

- ☐ "1st Prize" ribbon
- ☐ Bell
- ☐ Butterfly
- ☐ Cactus
- ☐ Cherry
- ☐ Cracked pot
- ☐ Duck
- ☐ Fire hydrant
- ☐ Fish
- ☐ Giraffe
- ☐ Key
- ☐ Lion
- ☐ Lobster
- ☐ Moon
- ☐ Mouse
- ☐ Painted egg
- ☐ Ring
- ☐ Rooster
- ☐ Sea horse
- ☐ Seal
- ☐ Spiderweb
- ☐ Tepee
- ☐ Tiger
- ☐ Top hat
- ☐ Trunk
- ☐ Yellow bird
- ☐ Watering can
- ☐ Winter hat

Find Wendy on the Jack-O'-Lantern Farm and...

- ☐ Apple
- ☐ Baseball bat
- ☐ Birds (2)
- ☐ Bones (2)
- ☐ Bowling ball
- ☐ Cactus
- ☐ Carrot
- ☐ Egg
- ☐ Fat candle
- ☐ Fire hydrant
- ☐ Flashlight
- ☐ Frog
- ☐ Ghosts (2)
- ☐ Hoe
- ☐ Kangaroo
- ☐ Lawn mower
- ☐ Lollipop
- ☐ Lost boot
- ☐ Magnifying glass
- ☐ Mailbox
- ☐ Mask
- ☐ Mummy
- ☐ Pear
- ☐ Periscope
- ☐ Pig
- ☐ Rake
- ☐ Skunk
- ☐ Surfboard

All of Wendy's "Where Are They?" friends have come to visit her jack-o'-lantern farm.

Look for:

- Bone
- Boot
- Brooms (3)
- Candy cane
- Chicken
- Crayon
- Flowers (2)
- Heart
- Mouse
- Mushroom
- Nail
- Smallest jack-o'-lantern

WHERE'S WENDY?

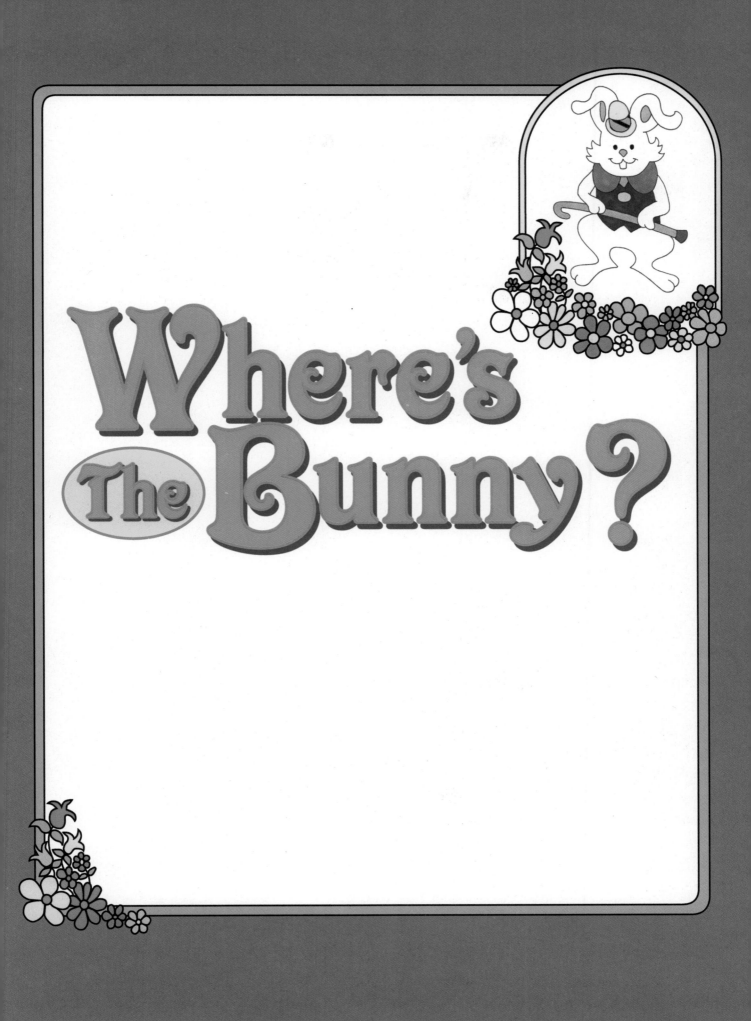

Find Bunny Honey at Wacky Farms and...

- [ ] Blackboard
- [ ] Bow ties (2)
- [ ] Bucket
- [ ] Burst balloon
- [ ] Cat
- [ ] Chickens (2)
- [ ] Cow
- [ ] Donkey
- [ ] Elephant
- [ ] Firefighter
- [ ] Fire hydrants (5)
- [ ] Flying balloon
- [ ] Flying bat
- [ ] Football player
- [ ] Ghost
- [ ] Giraffe
- [ ] Mouse
- [ ] Pencil
- [ ] Rocking chair
- [ ] Sailboats (4)
- [ ] Santa Claus
- [ ] Shovel
- [ ] Spaghetti
- [ ] Sunglasses
- [ ] Top hats (4)
- [ ] Truck tires (4)
- [ ] Turtle
- [ ] Umbrellas (2)
- [ ] Umpire
- [ ] Watering cans (2)

Find Bunny Honey at the
Costume Party
and...

- ☐ Apple
- ☐ Arrow
- ☐ Barrel
- ☐ Basket
- ☐ Beaver
- ☐ Bells (2)
- ☐ Broom
- ☐ Cactus (2)
- ☐ Clothespin
- ☐ Coffeepot
- ☐ Crown
- ☐ Ear of corn
- ☐ Egg
- ☐ Football
- ☐ Fork
- ☐ Frog
- ☐ Headless dancer
- ☐ Hot dog
- ☐ Ice-cream pop
- ☐ Ice skate
- ☐ Kite
- ☐ Lollipop
- ☐ Magnifying glass
- ☐ Pencils (2)
- ☐ Pizza
- ☐ Roller skates
- ☐ Skateboards (2)
- ☐ Tepee
- ☐ Yellow birds (2)

Find Bunny Honey in the
Bunny Parade
and...

- ☐ Accordion
- ☐ Bagpipes
- ☐ Banjo
- ☐ Birdcage
- ☐ Bone
- ☐ Boomerang
- ☐ Bowling ball
- ☐ Candy cane
- ☐ Carrots (11)
- ☐ Chocolate bunny
- ☐ Clown
- ☐ Covered wagon
- ☐ Drums (3)
- ☐ Flowerpot
- ☐ Ghost
- ☐ Guitar
- ☐ Harp
- ☐ Jack-o'-lantern
- ☐ Knight
- ☐ Light bulbs (2)
- ☐ Mouse
- ☐ Mummy
- ☐ Owl
- ☐ Painted eggs (12)
- ☐ Paper airplane
- ☐ Skateboard
- ☐ Sled
- ☐ Snowman
- ☐ Turtle
- ☐ Whistle
- ☐ Xylophone

Find **Bunny Honey** at the **Factory** and...

- ☐ Apple
- ☐ Arrow
- ☐ Baseball bat
- ☐ Basketball
- ☐ Birds (6)
- ☐ Black jelly beans (3)
- ☐ Candle
- ☐ Carrot
- ☐ Chimney
- ☐ Clothespins (2)
- ☐ Fish
- ☐ Flower
- ☐ Football player
- ☐ Handbag
- ☐ Igloo
- ☐ Knight
- ☐ Lost shoe
- ☐ Monster
- ☐ Pencil
- ☐ Pig
- ☐ Referee
- ☐ Snake
- ☐ Spear
- ☐ Top hat
- ☐ Turtle
- ☐ Umbrella
- ☐ Vacuum cleaner
- ☐ Worm
- ☐ Zebra

Find Bunny Honey at the Honey Bunny Hotel and...

- [ ] Balloons (3)
- [ ] Basketball
- [ ] Bowling ball
- [ ] Burned-out light
- [ ] Cactus
- [ ] Carrots (3)
- [ ] Chef
- [ ] Crack in egg
- [ ] Diving board
- [ ] Elephant
- [ ] Fish
- [ ] Frog
- [ ] Giraffe
- [ ] Jack-o'-lantern
- [ ] Ladders (3)
- [ ] Lifeguard
- [ ] Mouse
- [ ] Painter
- [ ] Parachute
- [ ] Periscope
- [ ] Pole vaulter
- [ ] Santa bunny
- [ ] Scarecrow
- [ ] Skateboard
- [ ] Snake
- [ ] Star
- [ ] Telescope
- [ ] Tree
- [ ] Yellow birds (4)

Find Bunny Honey on the
Bunny Trail
and...

- [ ] Apple
- [ ] Arrow
- [ ] Baskets (2)
- [ ] Bat
- [ ] Bell
- [ ] Bone
- [ ] Book
- [ ] Chimney
- [ ] Clock
- [ ] Crocodile
- [ ] Cup
- [ ] Drum
- [ ] Flowerpot
- [ ] Flying carpet
- [ ] Ghost
- [ ] Heart
- [ ] Helicopter
- [ ] Ice-cream cone
- [ ] Palm tree
- [ ] Rooster
- [ ] Sheep
- [ ] Ship in a bottle
- [ ] Sled
- [ ] Surfer
- [ ] Toaster
- [ ] Turtle
- [ ] Umbrella
- [ ] Wagon
- [ ] Windmill
- [ ] Wreath

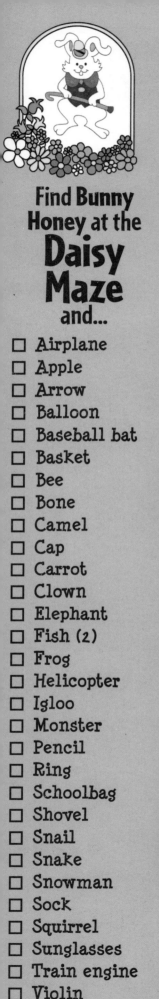

Find Bunny Honey at the **Daisy Maze** and...

- ☐ Airplane
- ☐ Apple
- ☐ Arrow
- ☐ Balloon
- ☐ Baseball bat
- ☐ Basket
- ☐ Bee
- ☐ Bone
- ☐ Camel
- ☐ Cap
- ☐ Carrot
- ☐ Clown
- ☐ Elephant
- ☐ Fish (2)
- ☐ Frog
- ☐ Helicopter
- ☐ Igloo
- ☐ Monster
- ☐ Pencil
- ☐ Ring
- ☐ Schoolbag
- ☐ Shovel
- ☐ Snail
- ☐ Snake
- ☐ Snowman
- ☐ Sock
- ☐ Squirrel
- ☐ Sunglasses
- ☐ Train engine
- ☐ Violin

Find Bunny Honey at the
Great Egg Roll
and...

- [ ] Ant
- [ ] Bee
- [ ] Clothespin
- [ ] Dogs (2)
- [ ] Duck
- [ ] Elephant
- [ ] Feather
- [ ] Fish
- [ ] Flamingo
- [ ] Football
- [ ] Fried egg
- [ ] Frog
- [ ] Helmet
- [ ] Horse
- [ ] Kangaroo
- [ ] Kite
- [ ] Magnifying glass
- [ ] Meatballs
- [ ] Paintbrush
- [ ] Raccoon
- [ ] Rhinoceros
- [ ] Scarves (2)
- [ ] Seal
- [ ] Skateboard
- [ ] Snake
- [ ] Spaceship
- [ ] Sunglasses
- [ ] Top hat
- [ ] Toucan
- [ ] Walrus

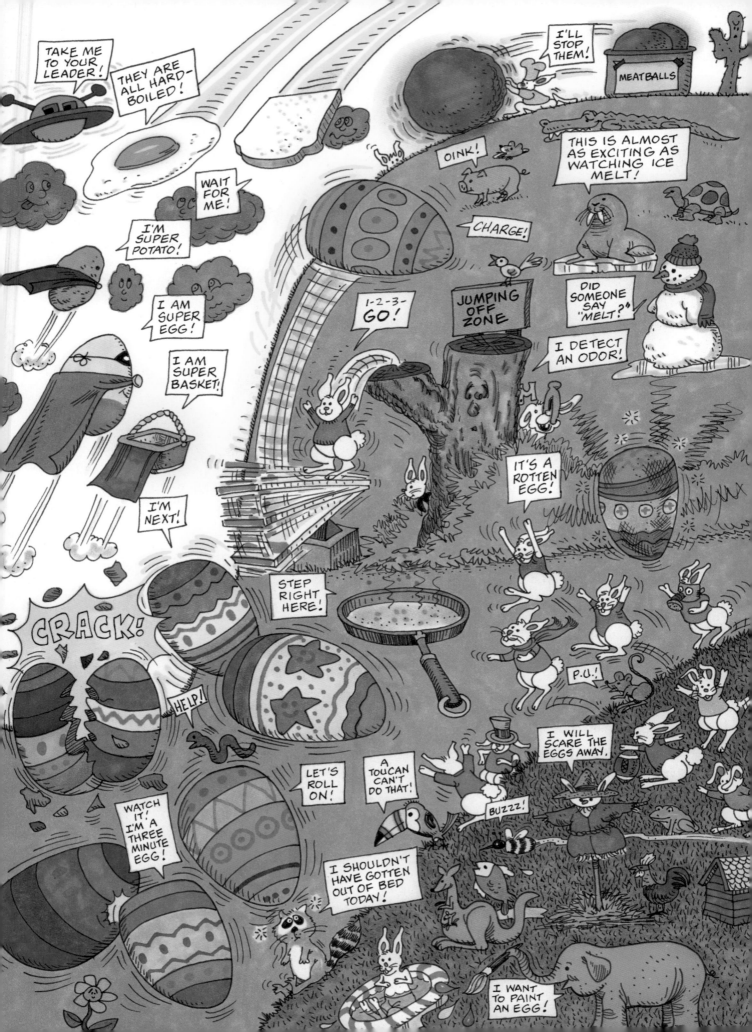

Find Bunny Honey at the
Spring Sale
and...

- ☐ Arrow
- ☐ Astronaut
- ☐ Banana peel
- ☐ Basket
- ☐ Birdcage
- ☐ Boxing glove
- ☐ Cactus
- ☐ Candle
- ☐ Centipede
- ☐ Chef
- ☐ Clothespin
- ☐ Clown
- ☐ Crown
- ☐ Fishing pole
- ☐ Flowerpot
- ☐ Ghost
- ☐ Horse
- ☐ Humpty Dumpty
- ☐ Igloo
- ☐ Lamp
- ☐ Monkey
- ☐ Mouse
- ☐ Octopus
- ☐ Owl
- ☐ Pies (2)
- ☐ Pirate
- ☐ Police officer
- ☐ Rooster
- ☐ Sailor hat
- ☐ Shopping bags (3)
- ☐ Sofa

Find **Bunny Honey** in the
Great Outdoors
and...

- ☐ Arrow
- ☐ Balloon
- ☐ Birds (3)
- ☐ Boots (3)
- ☐ Envelope
- ☐ Flying bat
- ☐ Football helmet
- ☐ Heart
- ☐ Hockey stick
- ☐ Horseshoe
- ☐ Ice skate
- ☐ Key
- ☐ Mitten
- ☐ Mushrooms (3)
- ☐ Periscope
- ☐ Pocketknife
- ☐ Pocket watch
- ☐ Roller skates
- ☐ Sailboat
- ☐ Scarf
- ☐ Skateboard
- ☐ Sled
- ☐ Star
- ☐ Tepee
- ☐ Unicorn
- ☐ Watering can
- ☐ Wooden fish
- ☐ Wooden rabbit
- ☐ Worms (2)

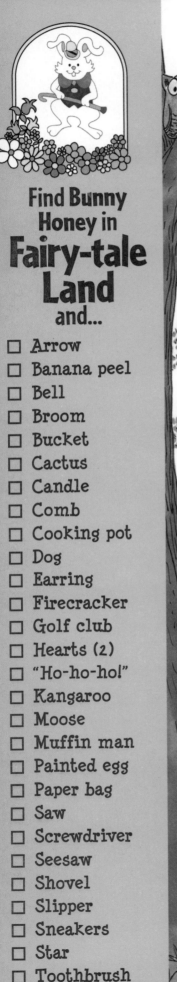

Find Bunny Honey in
Fairy-tale Land
and...

- ☐ Arrow
- ☐ Banana peel
- ☐ Bell
- ☐ Broom
- ☐ Bucket
- ☐ Cactus
- ☐ Candle
- ☐ Comb
- ☐ Cooking pot
- ☐ Dog
- ☐ Earring
- ☐ Firecracker
- ☐ Golf club
- ☐ Hearts (2)
- ☐ "Ho-ho-ho!"
- ☐ Kangaroo
- ☐ Moose
- ☐ Muffin man
- ☐ Painted egg
- ☐ Paper bag
- ☐ Saw
- ☐ Screwdriver
- ☐ Seesaw
- ☐ Shovel
- ☐ Slipper
- ☐ Sneakers
- ☐ Star
- ☐ Toothbrush
- ☐ Umbrellas (3)

Find Bunny Honey at the **Playground** and...

- ☐ Alien creature
- ☐ Balloons (2)
- ☐ Barbecue grill
- ☐ Baseball glove
- ☐ Binoculars
- ☐ Boat
- ☐ Books (2)
- ☐ Candle
- ☐ Cat
- ☐ Chef's hat
- ☐ Dart
- ☐ Fish (2)
- ☐ Frog
- ☐ Heart
- ☐ Helmets (2)
- ☐ Lost mittens (3)
- ☐ Mask
- ☐ Model airplane
- ☐ Monster
- ☐ Mouse
- ☐ Mushroom
- ☐ Nail
- ☐ Nest
- ☐ Owl
- ☐ Paper airplane
- ☐ Sailor hat
- ☐ Schoolbag
- ☐ Soccer ball
- ☐ Squirrel
- ☐ Yo-yo

Find Bunny Honey at this
Snowman Meltdown
and...

- ☐ Baseball
- ☐ Birds (4)
- ☐ Broom
- ☐ Butterfly
- ☐ Cage
- ☐ Candy cane
- ☐ Clown
- ☐ Drum
- ☐ Duck
- ☐ Fire hydrant
- ☐ Ghost
- ☐ Hammer
- ☐ Heart
- ☐ Hockey puck
- ☐ Jack-o'-lantern
- ☐ Key
- ☐ Kite
- ☐ Lollipop
- ☐ Milk container
- ☐ Pig
- ☐ Roller skater
- ☐ Rooster
- ☐ Sleeping cat
- ☐ Sock
- ☐ Stars (2)
- ☐ Sunglasses (2)
- ☐ Worm
- ☐ Wreath

Find **Bunny Honey** in this
Zany Egg Contest
and...

- [ ] Arrow
- [ ] Balloon
- [ ] Bear
- [ ] Books (3)
- [ ] Cat
- [ ] Chick
- [ ] Cup
- [ ] Dog
- [ ] Fallen leaf
- [ ] Feather
- [ ] Fish
- [ ] Flowerpot
- [ ] Flying bat
- [ ] Frying pan
- [ ] Ghost
- [ ] Horseshoe
- [ ] Key
- [ ] Kite
- [ ] Magnifying glass
- [ ] Neckties (2)
- [ ] Paper airplane
- [ ] Pencil
- [ ] Star
- [ ] Toothbrush
- [ ] Tree stump
- [ ] Turtle
- [ ] Zebra

Find Bunny Honey in the Bouncing Babies
Field
and...

- ☐ Alarm clock
- ☐ Baby bird
- ☐ Baby deer
- ☐ Baby elephants (2)
- ☐ Baby fish (2)
- ☐ Baby giraffe
- ☐ Baby human
- ☐ Baby kangaroo
- ☐ Baby mice (2)
- ☐ Baby monkey
- ☐ Baby owl
- ☐ Baby rabbits (3)
- ☐ Baby squirrel
- ☐ Baby turtles (2)
- ☐ Baby whale
- ☐ Baby worm
- ☐ Bone
- ☐ Books (2)
- ☐ Bowling pin
- ☐ Chicks (2)
- ☐ Ducklings (2)
- ☐ Eggs (5)
- ☐ Hang glider
- ☐ Kittens (3)
- ☐ Lamb
- ☐ Piglets (2)
- ☐ Puppies (2)
- ☐ Stork

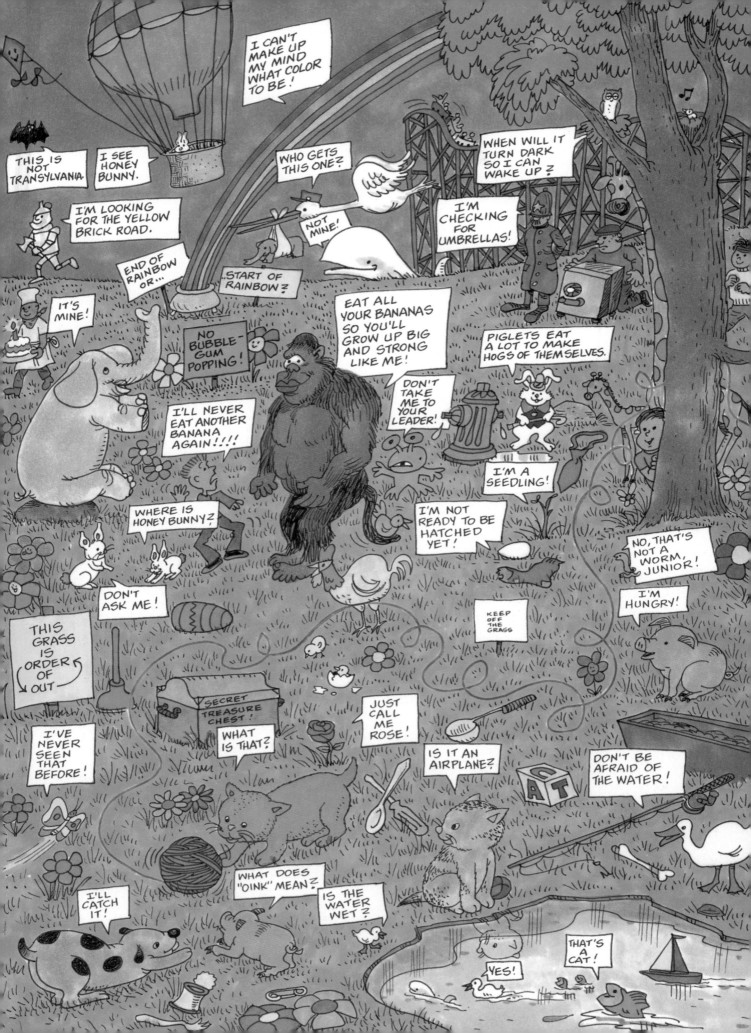